Best in Children's Books

Black Beauty and Ginger

by ANNA SEWELL

illustrated by PHOEBE ERICKSON

MY FIRST HOME

The first place that I can well remember was a large pleasant meadow with a pond of clear water in it. Over the hedge on one side we looked into a plowed field, and on the other we looked over a gate at our master's house.

Selections from *Black Beauty* chosen for young readers.

When I was young I lived upon my mother's milk, as I could not eat grass. In the daytime I ran by her side, and at night I lay down close by her. When it was hot, we used to stand by the pond in the shade of the trees, and when it was cold, we had a nice warm shed.

There were six young colts in the meadow, besides me. We used to gallop all together round and round the field.

One day, when there was a good deal of rough play—kicking and biting—my mother whinnied to me to come to

her, and then she said: "I wish you to pay attention to what I am going to say to you. The colts who live here are very good colts, but they are cart-horse colts, and of course they have not learned manners. You have been well bred and well born; your father had a great name in these parts, and your grandfather won the cup two years at the Newmarket races. I hope you will grow up gentle and good, and never learn bad ways. Do your work with a will, lift your feet up well when you trot, and never bite or kick even in play."

I have never forgotten my mother's advice. I knew she was a wise, gentle old horse, and our master thought a great deal of her.

I began to grow handsome. My coat was bright black, I had one white foot, and a pretty white star on my forehead.

When I was four years old, Squire Gordon of Birtwick Park came to look at me. He examined my eyes, my mouth, and my legs. Then I had to walk and trot and gallop before him.

He told my master that as soon as I was well broken in, he would buy me and take me to live in his stables at Birtwick Park.

My master said he would break me in himself, as he should not like me to be frightened or hurt.

Everyone may not know what breaking in is, therefore I will describe it. It means to teach a horse to wear a bridle —with a bit in his mouth—to wear a saddle and to carry on his back a man, a woman, or a child; to go just the way they wish, and to go quietly. Besides this he has to learn to wear a collar, and leather harness straps around his body, and to stand still while they are put on. Then he has to have a cart or a carriage fixed behind him, so that he cannot walk or trot without dragging it after him. He must go fast or slow—just as his driver wishes—even though he may be very tired or hungry. But worst of all, when his harness is once on he may neither jump for joy nor lie down in weariness. So you see this breaking in is a great thing.

Our master was a good, kind man. With pats, kind words, and gentle ways, and with rewards of nice oats, he went on to break me to bridle, saddle, and harness. So in time I got used to everything and could do my work as well as my mother.

Then Squire Gordon sent his groom to lead me to Birtwick Park. My master said: "Good-by. Be a good horse and always do your best." I could not say "good-by," so

I put my nose into his hand; he patted me kindly, and I left my first home.

"BLACK BEAUTY"

Squire Gordon's park was entered by a large iron gate, at which stood the lodge. Then you trotted along a smooth road, between clumps of large old trees, which brought you to the house and the gardens. Beyond this lay a small field, the old orchard, and the stables.

The groom put me into a large, square box stall in a roomy stable. The stall was clean, pleasant, and airy. It had a low rack for hay and a low manger for oats. It was

what is called a loose box because the horse that is put into it is not tied up but left loose, to do as he likes.

In the stall next to mine stood a fat gray pony, with a thick mane and tail, a very pretty little head, and a pert little nose.

I put my head up to the iron rails at the top of my box, and said: "How do you do? What is your name?"

"My name is Merrylegs. I carry the young ladies, Miss Flora and Miss Jessie, on my back, and sometimes I take our mistress out in the pony cart."

Just then a horse's head looked over from the stall beyond; the ears were laid back, and the eyes looked rather ill-tempered. This was a tall chestnut mare, with a long handsome neck. She looked across at me and said:

"So it is you who have turned me out of my box."

"I beg your pardon," I said, "I have turned no one out; the man who brought me put me here. It is my wish to live at peace."

"Well," said the mare, "we shall see."

Later, Merrylegs told me about the chestnut mare: "Ginger has a bad habit of biting and snapping; that is why they call her Ginger. One day, when she was in the loose box, she bit the groom, James, in the arm. Miss Flora and Miss Jessie were afraid to come to the stable to see me—for fear of Ginger. So it is Ginger's own fault that she did not stay in that box. If all she says is true, she must have been very ill-used before she came here. She says no one was ever kind to her. But I think she should be good-tempered here. I am twelve years old," went on Merrylegs. "I know a great deal, and I can tell you there is not a better place for a horse all round the country than this. John is the best head groom that ever was; and you never saw such a kind boy as James is."

The next morning John took me into the yard and gave me a good grooming. The Squire came to look at me, and seemed pleased. He told John to ride me around after breakfast and try my paces.

We had a splendid gallop, and as we came back through the park we met the Squire and Mrs. Gordon walking. They stopped, and John jumped off.

"Well, John, how does he go?"

"First-rate, sir," answered John. "He is as fleet as a deer, and has a fine spirit too; but the lightest touch of the rein will guide him. It is my opinion he has not been frightened or ill-used while he was young."

The next day I was brought up to the house for my new master. I remembered my mother's counsel and my good old master's, and I tried to do exactly what the Squire wanted me to do. I found he was a very good rider, and thoughtful for his horse too. When he came home, the lady was at the Hall door as he rode up.

"Well, my dear," she said, "how do you like him?"

"He is exactly what John said," he replied. "A pleasanter creature I never wish to mount. What shall we call him?"

"He is black as ebony," said she, "and he is really quite a beauty. What do you say to calling him Black Beauty?"

The Squire was pleased with the name, and so I became "Black Beauty."

GINGER

A few days after this I had to go out with Ginger in the carriage. I wondered how we should get on together, but except for laying her ears back when I was led up to her, she behaved very well. She did her work honestly, and did her full share; and I never wish to have a better partner in double harness. After we had been out two or three times together, we grew quite friendly and sociable.

It was a great treat for us, on fine Sundays in the summertime, to be turned out into the small field or the old orchard. The grass was so cool and soft to our feet, the air so sweet, and the freedom to do as we liked was so pleasant —to gallop, to lie down and roll over on our backs, or to nibble the sweet grass. It was a very good time for talking, as we stood together under the apple trees.

One day when Ginger and I were standing alone in the shade, Ginger wanted to know all about my bringing up and breaking in, and I told her.

"Well," said she, "if I had had your bringing up I might have had as good a temper as you, but it has all been so different with me.

"I never had anyone, horse or man, that was kind to me. I was taken from my mother as soon as I was weaned, and put with a lot of other young colts. There was no kind master like yours to look after me, and talk to me, and bring me nice things to eat. The man that had the care of us only thought to see that we had plenty to eat, and shelter in the winter. A footpath ran through our field, and very often the big boys, who were allowed to pass through, would fling stones at us, to make us gallop. I was never hit, but the stones made me more wild, and I settled it in my mind that boys were my enemies.

"When it came to breaking in—that was a bad time for me. Several men came to catch me, and at last they closed me in, at one corner of the field. One man caught me by the forelock; another caught me by the nose and held it so tight I could hardly draw my breath. Then still another man took my underjaw in his hard hand and wrenched my mouth open. And so, by force, they got the halter and the bar into my mouth. Then one dragged me along by the halter, while another flogged me from behind.

"I was highbred and had a good deal of spirit, and I know I was very wild and gave them plenty of trouble. After that, it was dreadful to be shut up in a stall day after day instead of having my liberty. You know yourself it's bad enough when you have a kind master and plenty of coaxing, but there was nothing of that sort for me.

"My master used to boast that he had never found a horse who could throw him. There was no gentleness in him but only hardness, and I felt from the first that what he wanted was to wear all the spirit out of me, and just make me into a quiet, humble, obedient piece of horse-flesh.

"Horseflesh! Yes, that is all he thought about me." And Ginger stamped her foot as if the very thought of him made her angry. Then she went on: "After my breaking in, I was matched with another chestnut horse and sold to

12

a fashionable London gentleman. This gentleman and his coachman wanted us to look stylish, so we were driven with a tight checkrein. You who have never had a checkrein on don't know what it is, but I can tell you it is dreadful.

"I like to toss my head and hold it as high as any horse; but fancy now, yourself, if you tossed your head up high and were obliged to hold it there, for hours together, not able to move it at all, except, with a jerk, still higher.

"I was willing to work, and ready to work hard too; but to be tormented for nothing but their notion of being *stylish* angered me. Besides the soreness in my mouth and the pain in my neck, I noticed that my breathing was affected. I grew more restless and irritable, and I began to snap and kick when anyone came to harness me. One day, as they had just buckled us into the carriage, and were straining my head up with that rein, I began to plunge and kick with all my might. I soon broke a lot of harness and kicked myself clear. So that was the end of that place.

"In my next place a hard-tempered, hard-handed groom wanted to make me afraid of him, and he hit me with his riding whip, his stable broom, or whatever he might have in his hand. After awhile, he dared not come into my stall. Either my heels or my teeth were ready for him, and he knew it. So I was sold again.

"I came here not long before you did, but I had then made up my mind that men were my natural enemies, and that I must defend myself.

"It's very different here. I bit James once, pretty sharp, but John said: 'Try her with kindness.' And instead of punishing me as I expected, James came to me, with his arm bound up, and brought me a bran mash and stroked me. And I have never snapped at him since, and I won't either."

I felt very sorry for Ginger. However, as the weeks went on, I found that she grew much more gentle and cheerful. She had lost the watchful, defiant look that she used to turn on any strange person who came near her.

Then one day James said, "I do believe that mare is getting fond of me. She quite whinnied after me this morning when I was rubbing her forehead."

"Aye, aye, Jim," said John, "she'll be as good as Black Beauty, by and by."

Squire Gordon noticed the change too, and one day when he got out of the carriage and came to speak to us as he often did, he stroked her beautiful neck. "Well, my pretty one, how do things go with you now? You are a good bit happier than when you came to us, I think."

She put her nose up to him in a friendly, trustful way,

while he rubbed it gently.

"We shall make a cure of her, John," he said.

A STORMY DAY

One day, late in the autumn, the Squire had a long journey to go, on business. I was hitched to the dogcart, and John went with his master. There had been a great deal of rain, and now the wind was very high, and blew the leaves across the road in a shower. We went along merrily until we came to the toll bar and the low wooden bridge. The river banks were rather high, so the bridge went across just level. If the river was full, the water would come nearly up to the woodwork and planks. The man at the gate said the river was rising fast, and he feared it would be a bad night.

Many of the meadows were under water, and in one low part of the road, the water was halfway up to my knees. When we got to the town, I had a good rest and feed, but as the master's business engaged him a long time we did not start for home till rather late in the afternoon. The wind was then much higher, and I heard the master say to

John that he had never been out in such a storm; and so I thought too, as we went along the skirts of a wood, where the great branches were swaying about like twigs, and the rushing sound was terrible.

"I wish we were well out of this wood," said my master.

"Yes, sir," said John, "it would be rather awkward if one of these branches came down upon us."

The words were scarcely out of his mouth, when there was a groan, and a crack, and a splitting sound; and tearing, crashing down among the other trees came an oak, torn up by the roots, and it fell right across the road just before us. I will never say I was not frightened, for I was. I stopped still, and I believe I trembled; of course I did not turn round or run away; I was not brought up to that. John jumped out and was in a moment at my head.

"What's to be done now?" asked my master.

"Well, sir, there will be nothing for it, but to go back to the four crossways, and that will be a good six miles before we get round to the wooden bridge again."

So back we went and round by the crossroads; but by the time we got to the bridge it was very nearly dark. We could just see that the water was over the middle of it; but as that happened sometimes, when the floods were out, master did not stop. We were going along at a good pace, but the moment my feet touched the first part of the bridge, I felt sure there was something wrong. I dared not go forward, and I made a dead stop. "Go on, Beauty," said my master, and he gave me a touch with the whip, but I dared not stir; he gave me a sharp cut; I jumped, but I dared not go forward.

"There's something wrong, sir," said John, and he sprang out of the dogcart and came to my head and looked all about. He tried to lead me forward. "Come on, Beauty. What's the matter?" Of course I could not tell him, but I knew very well that the bridge was not safe.

Just then the man at the tollgate on the other side ran out of the house, tossing a torch about like one mad.

"Hoy, hoy, hoy, halloo, stop!" he cried.

"What's the matter?" shouted my master.

"The bridge is broken in the middle, and part of it is carried away; if you come on you'll be into the river."

"Thank God!" said my master. "You Beauty!" said John, and took the bridle and gently turned me round to the right-hand road by the riverside. The sun had set some time; the wind seemed to have lulled off after that furious blast which tore up the tree. It grew darker and darker, stiller and stiller. I trotted quietly along, the wheels hardly making a sound on the soft road.

At last we came to the Park gates, and found the gardener looking out for us. He said that the mistress had been in a dreadful way ever since dark, fearing some accident had happened.

We saw a light at the Hall door and at the upper windows, and as we came up the mistress ran out, saying: "Are you really safe, my dear? Oh! I have been so anxious, fancying all sorts of things. Have you had no accident?"

"No, my dear; but if your Black Beauty had not been wiser than we were, we should all have been carried down the river at the wooden bridge." I heard no more, as they went into the house, and John took me to the stable. Oh! what a good supper he gave me that night, a good bran mash and some crushed beans with my oats, and such a thick bed of straw; and I was glad of it, for I was tired.

THE FIRE

It was decided, by my master and mistress, to pay a visit to some friends who lived about forty-six miles from our home, and young James was to drive them. James was to leave us and go as head groom to the Squire's brother-in-law; and in the meantime he was to get all the practice in driving that could be given to him.

The first day, Ginger and I traveled thirty-two miles. There were some long, steep hills, but James drove so carefully and thoughtfully that were we not at all harassed.

We stopped once or twice on the road, and just as the sun was going down we reached the town where we were to spend the night. We stopped at the principal hotel, which was in the market place. We drove under an arch-way into a long yard, at the further end of which were the stables and coach houses. Two hostlers came to take us out. The head hostler, a pleasant little old man, led me to a long stable, with six or eight stalls in it and two or three horses. The other, younger man brought Ginger. James stood by while we were being rubbed down; and he and the elder hostler talked. From this conversation I learned that the old man was wise in the ways of horses. When the younger hostler had finished grooming Ginger, and had brought our oats, James and the old man left the stable together.

Later on in the evening a traveler's horse was brought in by the second hostler, and while he was cleaning him a young man with a pipe in his mouth lounged into the stable to gossip.

"I say, Towler," said the hostler, "just run up the ladder into the loft and put some hay down into this horse's rack, will you? Only lay down your pipe."

"All right," said the other, and went up through the trap door; and I heard him step across the floor overhead and put down the hay. James came in to look at us the last thing, and then the door was locked.

I cannot say how long I had slept, nor what time in the night it was, but I woke up very uncomfortable, though I hardly knew why. I got up. The air seemed all thick and choking. I heard Ginger coughing, and one of the other horses moved about restlessly. It was quite dark, and I could see nothing, but the stable was full of smoke and I hardly knew how to breathe.

The trap door had been left open, and I thought that was the place it came through. I listened and heard a rushing sort of noise, and a low crackling and snap did not know what it was, but there was someth sound so strange that it made me tremble all other horses were now all awake were p halters, others were st

At last I heard

burst into the stable with a lantern, and began to untie the horses, and try to lead them out; but he seemed in such a hurry and so frightened himself that he frightened me still more. The first horse would not go with him; he tried the second and third; they too would not stir. He came to me next and tried to drag me out of the stall by force; of course that was no use. He tried us all by turns and then left the stable.

No doubt we were very foolish, but danger seemed to be all round, and there was nobody we knew to trust in, and all was strange and uncertain. The fresh air that had come in through the open door made it easier to breathe, but the rushing sound overhead grew louder, and as I looked upward through the bars of my empty rack I saw a red light flickering on the wall. Then I heard a cry of "Fire" outside, and the old hostler quietly and quickly came in. He got one horse out and went to another, but the flames were playing ___ d the trap door, and the roaring overhead was dreadful.

The next ___ I heard was James' voice, quiet and cheery, as it a___ ___s. "Come, my beauties, it is time for us to be off, so wa___ ___ and come along." I stood nearest the door, so he came ___ me first, patting me as he spoke. "Come, Beauty, on wi'h your bridle, my boy, we'll soon ___ of this smother." ___t was on in no time; then he took ___ff his neck, a___ ___d it lightly over my eyes, and ___ coaxing m___ ___e out of the stable. Safe in ___ slipped ___ my eyes, and shouted, ___dy! ___ ___ile I go back for the

A tall, broad man stepped forward and took me, and James darted back into the stable. I set up a shrill whinny as I saw him go. Ginger told me afterwards that whinny was the best thing I could have done for her, for had she not heard me outside she would never have had courage to come out.

There was much confusion in the yard: the horses being

got out of other stables, and the carriages and gigs being pulled out of houses and sheds, lest the flames should spread further. On the other side of the yard windows were thrown up, and people were shouting all sorts of things; but I kept my eye fixed on the stable door, where the smoke poured out thicker than ever, and I could see flashes of red light. Presently I heard above all the stir and din a loud, clear voice, which I knew was master's:

"James Howard! James Howard! Are you there?" There was no answer, but I heard a crash of something falling in the stable, and the next moment I gave a loud joyful neigh, for I saw James coming through the smoke leading Ginger.

"My brave lad!" said master, laying his hand on his shoulder. "Are you hurt?"

James shook his head, for he could not yet speak.

"Aye," said the big man who held me, "he is a brave lad, and no mistake."

"And now," said master, "when you have got your breath, James, we'll get out of this place as quickly as we can." We were moving towards the entry, when from the market place there came a sound of galloping feet and loud rumbling wheels.

"'Tis the fire engine! The fire engine!" shouted two or three voices. "Stand back, make way!" And clattering and thundering over the stones two horses dashed into the yard with the heavy engine behind them. The firemen leaped to the ground; there was no need to ask where the fire was—it was torching up in a great blaze from the roof.

We got out as fast as we could into the broad, quiet market place; the stars were shining, and except for the noise behind us, all was still. Master led the way to a large hotel on the other side; and as soon as the hostler came, he said, "James, I must now hasten to your mistress. I trust the horses entirely to you; order whatever you think is needed." And with that he was gone.

The next morning the master came to see how we were and to speak to James. Our mistress had been so much alarmed in the night that the journey was put off till the afternoon, so James had the morning on hand, and went first to the inn to see about our harness and the carriage, and then to hear more about the fire. When he came back, we heard him tell the hostler about it. At first no one could guess how the fire had been caused, but at last a man said he saw Dick Towler go into the stable with a pipe in his mouth, and when he came out he had not one. Then the younger hostler said he had asked Dick to go up the ladder to put down some hay, but told him to lay down his pipe first. Dick denied taking the pipe with him, but no one believed him. I remembered our John's rule, never to allow a pipe in the stable, and thought it ought to be the rule everywhere.

The rest of our journey was very easy, and a little after sunset we reached the house of my master's friend. We were taken into a clean, snug stable; there was a kind coachman, who made us very comfortable, and who seemed to think a good deal of James when he heard about the fire.

"There is one thing quite clear, young man," he said, "your horses know who they can trust. It is one of the hardest things in the world to get horses out of a stable when there is either fire or flood. I don't know why they won't come out, but they won't—not one in twenty."

We stopped two or three days at this place and then returned home. All went well on the journey; we were glad to be in our own stable again, and John was equally glad to see us.

Before he and James left us for the night, James said, "I wonder who is coming in my place?"

"Little Joe Green at the lodge."

"The gardener's son? Tom Green's boy? Why, he's a child!"

"He's fourteen and a half. He's small, but he's quick and willing and kind-hearted, too. I know the master would like to give him a chance."

"It will be six months before he can learn enough to be of much use. It will make you a great deal of work, John."

"Well," said John with a laugh, "work and I are very good friends. I was never afraid of work."

"You are a very good man," said James. "I wish I may ever be like you."

So Ginger and Merrylegs and I learned that our kind James was leaving us soon. We were very sorry to see him go.

GOING FOR THE DOCTOR

One night, a few days after James had left, I had eaten my hay and was lying down in my straw fast asleep, when I was suddenly roused by the stable bell ringing very loud. I heard the door of John's house open, and his feet running

up to the Hall. He was back again in no time; he unlocked the stable door, and came in, calling out, "Wake up, Beauty, you must go well now, if ever you did." And almost before I could think he had got the saddle on my back and the bridle on my head. He just ran round for his coat, and then took me at a quick trot up to the Hall door. The Squire stood there with a lamp in his hand.

"Now, John," he said, "ride for your life—that is, for your mistress' life. There is not a moment to lose; give this note to Doctor White; give your horse a rest at the inn, and be back as soon as you can."

John said, "Yes, sir," and was on my back in a minute.

The gardener who lived at the lodge had heard the bell ring, and was ready with the gate open, and away we went through the Park and through the village, and down the hill till we came to the river.

There was before us a long piece of level road by the riverside. John said to me, "Now, Beauty, do your best." And so I did; I wanted no whip nor spur, and for two miles I galloped as fast as I could lay my feet to the ground; I don't believe that my old grandfather who won the races at Newmarket could have gone faster. When we came to the bridge, John pulled me up a little and patted my neck. "Well done, Beauty! good old fellow," he said.

He would have let me go slower, but my spirit was up, and I was off again as fast as before. The air was frosty, the moon was bright, it was very pleasant. We came through a village, then through a dark wood, then uphill, then downhill, till after an eight miles' run we came to the town, through the streets and into the market place. It was all quite still except for the clatter of my feet on the stones—everybody was asleep. The church clock struck three as we drew up at Doctor White's door. John rang the bell twice, and then knocked at the door like thunder. A window was thrown up, and Doctor White, in his nightcap, put his head out and said, "What do you want?"

"Mrs. Gordon is very ill, sir; master wants you to go at once. He thinks she will die if you cannot get there—here is a note."

"Wait," he said, "I will come."

He shut the window, and was soon at the door.

"The worst of it is," he said, "that my horse has been out all day and is quite done up. What is to be done? Can I have your horse?"

"He has come at a gallop nearly all the way, sir, and I was to give him a rest here; but I think my master would not be against it if you think fit, sir."

"All right," he said, "I will soon be ready."

John stood by me and stroked my neck; I was very hot. The doctor came out with his riding whip.

"You need not take that, sir," said John. "Black Beauty will go till he drops. Take care of him, sir, if you can; I should not like any harm to come to him."

"No! no! John," said the doctor, "I hope not." And in

a minute we had left John far behind.

I will not tell about our way back; the doctor was a heavier man than John, and not so good a rider; however, I did my very best. When we came to the hill, the doctor drew me up. "Now, my good fellow," he said, "take some breath." I was glad he did, for I was nearly spent, but that breathing helped me on, and soon we were in the Park. Joe, the new groom, was at the lodge gate; my master was at the Hall door, for he had heard us coming. He spoke not a word. The doctor went into the house with him, and Joe led me to the stable.

I was glad to get home. My legs shook under me, and I could only stand and pant. I had not a dry hair on my body, and I steamed all over. Poor Joe! He was young and small, and as yet he knew very little; but I am sure he did the very best he knew. He rubbed my legs and my chest, but he did not put my warm cloth on me—he thought I was so hot I should not like it. Then he gave me a pailful of water to drink; it was cold and very good, and I drank it all. Then he gave me some hay and some oats; and thinking he had done right, he went away.

Soon I began to shake and tremble, and turned deadly cold. My legs ached, my loins ached, and my chest ached, and I felt sore all over. Oh! how I wished for my warm thick cloth as I stood and trembled. I wished for John, but he had eight miles to walk, so I lay down in my straw and tried to go to sleep. After a long while I heard John at the door; I gave a low moan, for I was in great pain. He was at my side in a moment, stooping down by me. I could not tell him how I felt; but he seemed to know it all. He

covered me up with two or three warm cloths, and then ran to the house for some hot water. He made me some warm gruel, which I drank, and then I think I went to sleep.

John seemed to be very much put out. I heard him say to himself over and over again, "Stupid boy! Stupid boy! No cloth put on, and I dare say the water was cold too. Boys are no good."

I was now very ill; a strong inflammation had attacked my lungs, and I could not draw my breath without pain. John nursed me night and day; he would get up two or three times in the night to come to me. My master, too, often came to see me. "My poor Beauty," he said one day, "my good horse, you saved your mistress' life, Beauty! Yes, you saved her life." I was very glad to hear that, for it seems the doctor had said if we had been a little longer it would have been too late. John told my master he never saw a horse go so fast in his life; it seemed as if the horse knew what was the matter. Of course I did, though John thought not. At least I knew as much as this: that John and I must go at the top of our speed, and that it was for the sake of the mistress.

I do not know how long I was ill. Mr. Bond, the horse doctor, came every day. One day he bled me; I felt very faint after it, and thought I should die, and I believe they all thought so too.

Ginger and Merrylegs had been moved into the other stable, so that I might be quiet, for the fever made me very quick of hearing. Any little noise seemed quite loud, and I could tell everyone's footsteps going to and from the house. I knew all that was going on. One night John had to give me medicine. Thomas Green, the gardener, came in to help him. After I had taken it and John had made me as comfortable as he could, he said he should stay half an hour to see how the medicine settled. Thomas said he would stay with him, so they went and sat down on a bench that had been brought into Merrylegs' stall, and put down the lantern at their feet that I might not be disturbed with the light.

For a while both men sat silent, and then Tom Green said in a low voice: "I wish, John, you'd say a bit of a kind word to Joe; the boy is quite broken-hearted. He can't eat his meals, and he can't smile. He says he knows it was all his fault, though he is sure he did the best he knew, and he says if Beauty dies no one will ever speak to him again.

It goes to my heart to hear him. I think you might give him just a word. He is not a bad boy."

After a short pause, John said slowly, "You must not be too hard upon me, Tom. I know he meant no harm; I never said he did. I know he is not a bad boy. But you see that horse is the pride of my heart, to say nothing of his being such a favorite with the master and mistress. And to think that his life may be flung away in this manner is more than I can bear. But if you think I am hard on the boy I will try to give him a good word tomorrow—that is, I mean if Beauty is better."

I heard no more of this conversation, for the medicine did well and sent me to sleep. In the morning I felt better,

and after some weeks' rest I was back with Ginger, taking my master and mistress in the carriage.

John forgave Joe Green, and the lad went on very well. He learned quickly and was so attentive and careful that John began to trust him in many things.

So the longer I lived at Birtwick, the more proud and happy I felt at having such a place. Our master and mistress were respected and beloved by all who knew them. They were good and kind to everybody and everything; not only men and women, but horses and donkeys, dogs and cats, cattle and birds. There was no oppressed or ill-used creature that had not a friend in them.

Mother Goose
Nursery Rhymes

illustrated by

MARGUERITE DE ANGELI

See-saw, sacradown,
Which is the way to London town?
One foot up and the other foot down,
That is the way to London town.

Bow-wow, says the dog;
    Mew, mew, says the cat;
Grunt, grunt, goes the hog;
    And squeak goes the rat.

Tu-whu, says the owl;
    Caw, caw, says the crow;
Quack, quack, says the duck;
    And what sparrows say, you know.

So, with sparrows, and owls,
    With rats, and with dogs,
With ducks, and with crows,
    With cats, and with hogs,

A fine song I have made,
    To please you, my dear;
And if it's well sung,
    'Twill be charming to hear.

Blow, wind, blow! and go, mill, go!
That the miller may grind his corn;
That the baker may take it,
And into rolls make it,
And bring us some hot in the morn.

I had a little husband,
  No bigger than my thumb;
I put him in a pint-pot
  And there I bade him drum.

There was a little girl, and she had a little curl
Right in the middle of her forehead;
When she was good, she was very, very good,
But when she was bad, she was horrid.

There was an old woman who lived in a shoe,
She had so many children she didn't know what to do;
She gave them some broth without any bread;
She whipped them all soundly and put them to bed.

Monday's child is fair of face,
Tuesday's child is full of grace,
Wednesday's child is full of woe,
Thursday's child has far to go,
Friday's child is loving and giving,
Saturday's child works hard for his living,
And the child that is born on the Sabbath day
Is bonny and blithe, and good and gay.

Burnie bee, burnie bee,
Tell me when your wedding be?
If it be to-morrow day,
Take your wings and fly away.

There was a bee
    Sat on a wall;
He said he could hum,
    And that was all.

Smiling girls, rosy boys,
Come and buy my little toys—
Monkeys made of gingerbread,
And sugar-horses painted red.

43

See a pin and pick it up;
All the day you'll have good luck;
See a pin and let it lie,
Sure you'll want before you die.

March winds and April showers
Bring forth May flowers.

The Nightingale

by HANS CHRISTIAN ANDERSEN

illustrated by COLLEEN BROWNING

In China, as you know, the Emperor is Chinese, and all the people around him are Chinese too. It is many years since the story I am going to tell you happened, but that is all the more reason for telling it, lest it should be forgotten.

Text from *Hans Andersen's Fairy Tales*, translated by Mrs. Edgar Lucas. Children's Illustrated Classics. Reprinted by permission of the publishers, E. P. Dutton & Company, Inc.

45

The Emperor's palace was the most beautiful thing in the world; it was made entirely of the finest porcelain, very costly, but at the same time so fragile that it could only be touched with the very greatest care. There were the most extraordinary flowers to be seen in the garden; the most beautiful ones had little silver bells tied to them, which tinkled perpetually, so that one should not pass the flowers without looking at them. Every little detail in the garden had been most carefully thought out, and it was so big that even the gardener himself did not know where it ended. If one went on walking, one came to beautiful woods with lofty trees and deep lakes. The wood extended to the sea, which was deep and blue, deep enough for large ships to sail up right under the branches of the trees.

Among these trees lived a Nightingale, which sang so deliciously that even the poor fisherman who had plenty of other things to do lay still to listen to it, when he was out at night drawing in his nets.

"Heavens, how beautiful it is!" he said, but then he had to attend to his business, and forgot it. The next night, when he heard it again, he would again exclaim: "Heavens, how beautiful it is!"

Travelers came to the Emperor's capital from every country in the world; they admired everything very much, especially the palace and the gardens, but when they heard the Nightingale they all said: "This is better than anything!"

When they got home they described it, and the learned ones wrote many books about the town, the palace, and the garden, but nobody forgot the Nightingale; it was always put above everything else. Those among them who were poets wrote the most beautiful poems, all about the Nightingale in the woods by the deep blue sea. These books went all over the world, and in the course of time some of them reached the Emperor. He sat in his golden chair reading and reading, and nodding his head, well pleased to hear such beautiful descriptions of the town, the palace, and the garden. "But the Nightingale is the best of all," he read.

"What is this?" said the Emperor. "The Nightingale? Why, I know nothing about it. Is there such a bird in my kingdom, and in my own garden into the bargain, and I have never heard of it? Imagine my having to discover this from a book!"

Then he called his gentleman-in-waiting, who was so grand that when any one of a lower rank dared to speak to him, or to ask him a question, he only would answer "P," which means nothing at all.

"There is said to be a very wonderful bird called a Nightingale here," said the Emperor. "They say that it is better than anything else in all my great kingdom! Why have I never been told anything about it?"

"I have never heard it mentioned," said the gentleman-in-waiting. "It has never been presented at court."

"I wish it to appear here this evening to sing to me," said the Emperor. "The whole world knows what I am possessed of, and I know nothing about it!"

"I have never heard it mentioned before," said the gentleman-in-waiting. "I will seek it, and I will find it!"

But where was it to be found? The gentleman-in-waiting

ran upstairs and downstairs and in and out of all the rooms and corridors. No one of all those he met had ever heard anything about the Nightingale; so the gentleman-in-waiting ran back to the Emperor, and said that it must be a myth, invented by the writers of the books. "Your imperial majesty must not believe everything that is written; books are often mere inventions, even if they do not belong to what we call the black art!"

"But the book in which I read it is sent to me by the

powerful Emperor of Japan, so it can't be untrue. I will hear this Nightingale—I insist upon its being here tonight. I extend my most gracious protection to it, and if it is not forthcoming I will have the whole court trampled upon after supper!"

"Tsing-pe!" said the gentleman-in-waiting, and away he ran again, up and down all the stairs, in and out of all the rooms and corridors; half the court ran with him, for they

none of them wished to be trampled on. There was much questioning about this Nightingale, which was known to all the outside world, but to no one at court. At last they found a poor little maid in the kitchen. She said: "Oh, heavens, the Nightingale? I know it very well. Yes, indeed it can sing. Every evening I am allowed to take broken meat to my poor sick mother. She lives down by the shore. On my way back when I am tired I rest awhile in the wood, and then I hear the Nightingale. Its song brings the tears into my eyes; I feel as if my mother were kissing me!"

"Little kitchen maid," said the gentleman-in-waiting, "I will procure you a permanent position in the kitchen and permission to see the Emperor dining, if you will take us to the Nightingale. It is commanded to appear at court tonight."

Then they all went out into the wood where the Nightingale usually sang. Half the court was there. As they were going along at their best pace a cow began to bellow.

"Oh," said a young courtier, "there we have it. What wonderful power for such a little creature; I have certainly heard it before."

"No, those are the cows bellowing; we are a long way yet from the place."

Then the frogs began to croak in the marsh.

"Beautiful!" said the Chinese chaplain. "It is just like the tinkling of church bells."

"No, those are the frogs!" said the little kitchen maid. "But I think we shall soon hear it now!"

Then the Nightingale began to sing.

"There it is!" said the little girl. "Listen, listen, there it

sits!" And she pointed to a little grey bird up among the branches.

"Is it possible?" said the gentleman-in-waiting. "I should never have thought it was like that. How common it looks. Seeing so many grand people must have frightened all its colors away."

"Little Nightingale," called the kitchen maid quite loud, "our gracious Emperor wishes you to sing to him!"

"With the greatest pleasure!" said the Nightingale, warbling away in the most delightful fashion.

"It is just like crystal bells," said the gentleman-in-waiting. "Look at its little throat, how active it is. It is extraordinary that we have never heard it before! I am sure it will be a great success at court!"

"Shall I sing again to the Emperor?" said the Nightingale, who thought he was present.

"My precious little Nightingale," said the gentleman-in-waiting, "I have the honor to command your attendance at a court festival tonight, where you will charm his gracious majesty the Emperor with your fascinating singing."

"It sounds best among the trees," said the Nightingale, but it went with them willingly when it heard that the Emperor wished it.

The palace had been brightened up for the occasion. The walls and the floors, which were all of china, shone by the light of many thousand golden lamps. The most beautiful flowers, all of the tinkling kind, were arranged in the corridors; there was hurrying to and fro, and a great draught, but this was just what made the bells ring—one's ears were full of the tinkling. In the middle of the large reception room where the Emperor sat, a golden rod had been fixed, on which the Nightingale was to perch. The whole court was assembled, and the little kitchen maid had been permitted to stand behind the door, as she now had the actual title of cook. They were all dressed in their best; everybody's eyes were turned towards the little grey bird at which the Emperor was nodding. The Nightingale sang delightfully, and the tears came into the Emperor's eyes, nay, they rolled down his cheeks, and then the Nightingale sang more beautifully than ever—its notes touched all hearts. The Emperor was charmed, and said the Nightingale should have his gold slipper to wear round its neck. But the Nightingale declined with thanks; it had already been sufficiently rewarded.

"I have seen tears in the eyes of the Emperor—that is my richest reward. The tears of an Emperor have a wonderful power! God knows I am sufficiently recompensed!" And then it again burst into its sweet heavenly song.

"That is the most delightful coquetting I have ever seen!" said the ladies, and they took some water into their mouths to try and make the same gurgling, when anyone spoke to them, thinking so to equal the Nightingale. Even the lackeys and the chambermaids announced that they were satisfied, and that is saying a great deal; they are always the most difficult people to please. Yes indeed, the Nightingale had made a sensation. It was to stay at court now, and to have its own cage, as well as liberty to walk out twice a day and once in the night. It always had twelve footmen, with each one holding a ribbon which was tied round its leg. There was not much pleasure in an outing of that sort.

The whole town talked about the marvelous bird, and if two people met, one said to the other "Night," and the other answered "Gale," and then they sighed, perfectly understanding each other. Eleven cheesemongers' children were called after it, but they had not got a voice among them.

One day a large parcel came for the Emperor; outside was written the word "Nightingale."

"Here we have another new book about this celebrated bird," said the Emperor. But it was no book; it was a little work of art in a box, an artificial Nightingale, exactly like the living one, but it was studded all over with diamonds, rubies, and sapphires.

When the bird was wound up it could sing one of the songs the real Nightingale sang, and it wagged its tail which glittered with silver and gold. A ribbon was tied round its neck on which was written: "The Emperor of Japan's Nightingale is very poor compared to the Emperor of China's."

Everybody said: "Oh, how beautiful!" And the person who brought the artificial bird immediately received the title of Imperial Nightingale-Carrier-in-Chief.

"Now they must sing together; what a duet that will be."

Then they had to sing together, but they did not get on very well, for the real Nightingale sang in its own way, and the artificial one could only sing waltzes.

"There is no fault in that," said the music master. "It is perfectly in time and correct in every way!"

Then the artificial bird had to sing alone. It was just as great a success as the real one, and then it was so much prettier to look at; it glittered like bracelets and breast-pins.

It sang the same tune three and thirty times over, and yet it was not tired; people would willingly have heard it from the beginning again, but the Emperor said that the real one must have a turn now—but where was it? No one had noticed that it had flown out of the open window, back to its own green woods.

"But what is the meaning of this?" said the Emperor.

All the courtiers railed at it and said it was a most ungrateful bird.

"We have got the best bird, though," said they, and

then the artificial bird had to sing again, and this was the thirty-fourth time that they heard the same tune, but they did not know it thoroughly even yet, because it was so difficult.

The music master praised the bird tremendously, and insisted that it was much better than the real Nightingale, not only in regard to the outside with all the diamonds, but the inside too.

"Because you see, my ladies and gentlemen, and the Emperor before all, in the real Nightingale you never know what you will hear, but in the artificial one everything is decided beforehand! So it is, and so it must remain—it can't be otherwise. You can account for things; you can open it and show the human ingenuity in arranging the waltzes, how they go, and how one note follows upon another!"

"Those are exactly my opinions," they all said, and the music master got leave to show the bird to the public the next Sunday. They were also to hear it sing, said the Emperor. So they heard it, and all became as enthusiastic over it as if they had drunk themselves merry on tea, because that is a thoroughly Chinese habit.

Then they all said "Oh," and stuck their forefingers in the air and nodded their heads; but the poor fisherman who had heard the real Nightingale said: "It sounds very nice, and it is very like the real one, but there is something wanting, we don't know what."

The real Nightingale was banished from the kingdom. The artificial bird had its place on a silken cushion, close to the Emperor's bed; all the presents it had received of gold and precious jewels were scattered round it. Its title had risen to be "Chief Imperial Singer of the Bedchamber," in rank number one, on the left side; for the Emperor reckoned that side the important one, where the heart was seated. And even an Emperor's heart is on the left side. The music master wrote five and twenty volumes

about the artificial bird; the treatise was very long, and written in all the most difficult Chinese characters. Everybody said they had read and understood it, for otherwise they would have been reckoned stupid, and then their bodies would have been trampled upon.

Things went on in this way for a whole year. The Emperor, the court, and all the other Chinese knew every little gurgle in the song of the artificial bird by heart; but they liked it all the better for this, and they could all join in the song themselves. Even the street boys sang "zizizi" and "cluck, cluck, cluck," and the Emperor sang it too.

But one evening when the bird was singing its best, and
the Emperor was lying in bed listening to it, something
gave way inside the bird with a *whizz*. Then a spring burst,
whirr went all the wheels and the music stopped. The
Emperor jumped out of bed and sent for his private physi-
cians, but what good could they do? Then they sent for
the watchmaker, and after a good deal of talk and examina-
tion, he got the works to go again somehow; but he said
it would have to be saved as much as possible, because it
was so worn out, and he could not renew the works so as
to be sure of the tune. This was a great blow! They only
dared to let the artificial bird sing once a year, and hardly
that; but then the music master made a little speech, using
all the most difficult words. He said it was just as good as
ever, and his saying it made it so.

Five years now passed, and then a great grief came upon
the nation, for they were all very fond of their Emperor,
and he was ill and could not live, it was said. A new
Emperor was already chosen, and people stood about in
the street, and asked the gentleman-in-waiting how their
Emperor was going on.

"P," answered he, shaking his head.

The Emperor lay pale and cold in his gorgeous bed; the
courtiers thought he was dead, and they all went off to
pay their respects to their new Emperor. The lackeys ran
off to talk matters over, and the chambermaids gave a
great coffee party. Cloth had been laid down in all the
rooms and corridors so as to deaden the sound of footsteps,
so it was very, very quiet. But the Emperor was not dead

yet. He lay stiff and pale in the gorgeous bed with its velvet hangings and heavy golden tassels. There was an open window high above him, and the moon streamed in upon the Emperor, and the artificial bird beside him.

The poor Emperor could hardly breathe—he seemed to have a weight on his chest. He opened his eyes and then he saw that it was Death sitting upon his chest, wearing his golden crown. In one hand he held the Emperor's golden sword and in the other his imperial banner. Round about, from among the folds of the velvet hangings, peered many curious faces; some were hideous, others gentle and pleasant. They were all the Emperor's good and bad deeds, which now looked him in the face when Death was weighing him down.

"Do you remember that?" whispered one after the other. "Do you remember this?" and they told him so many things that the perspiration poured down his face.

"I never knew that," said the Emperor. "Music, music, sound the great Chinese drums!" he cried, "that I may not hear what they are saying." But they went on and on, and Death sat nodding his head at everything that was said.

"Music, music!" shrieked the Emperor. "You precious little golden bird, sing, sing! I have loaded you with precious stones, and even hung my own golden slipper round your neck! Sing, I tell you, sing!"

But the bird stood silent; there was nobody to wind it up, so of course it could not go. Death continued to fix his stare upon the Emperor, and all was silent, so terribly silent.

Suddenly, close to the window, there was a burst of lovely song; it was the living Nightingale, perched on a branch outside. It had heard of the Emperor's need, and had come to bring comfort and hope to him. As it sang the faces round became fainter and fainter, and the blood coursed with fresh vigor in the Emperor's veins and through his feeble limbs. Even Death himself listened to the song and said: "Go on, little Nightingale, go on!"

"Yes, if you give me the gorgeous golden sword; yes, if you give me the imperial banner; yes, if you give me the Emperor's crown."

And Death gave back each of these treasures for a song, and the Nightingale went on singing. It sang about the quiet churchyard, where the roses bloom, where the elder flowers scent the air, and where the fresh grass is ever moistened anew by the tears of the mourner. This song brought to Death a longing for his own garden, and like a cold grey mist he passed out of the window.

"Thanks, thanks!" said the Emperor; "you heavenly little bird, I know you! I banished you from my kingdom, and yet you have charmed the evil visions away from my bed by your song, and even Death away from my heart! How can I ever repay you?"

"You have rewarded me," said the Nightingale. "I brought the tears to your eyes the very first time I ever sang to you, and I shall never forget it! Those are the jewels which gladden the heart of a singer; but sleep now, and wake up fresh and strong; I will sing to you!"

Then it sang again, and the Emperor fell into a sweet refreshing sleep. The sun shone in at his window, when he woke refreshed and well; none of his attendants had yet come back to him, for they thought he was dead, but the Nightingale still sat there singing.

"You must always stay with me!" said the Emperor. "You shall only sing when you like, and I will break the artificial bird into a thousand pieces!"

"Don't do that!" said the Nightingale. "It did all the good it could! Keep it as you have always done! I can't build my nest and live in this palace, but let me come whenever I like; then I will sit on the branch in the evening and sing to you. I will sing to cheer you and to make you thoughtful too; I will sing to you of the happy ones, and of those who suffer too. I will sing about the good and the evil, which are kept hidden from you. The little singing bird flies far and wide, to the poor fisherman, and the peasant's home, to people who are far from you and your court. I love your heart more than your crown, and yet there is an odor of sanctity round the crown too! I will come and I will sing to you! But you must promise me one thing!"

"Everything!" said the Emperor, who stood there in his imperial robes which he had just put on, and he held the sword heavy with gold upon his heart.

"One thing I ask you! Tell no one that you have a little bird who tells you everything—it will be better so!"

Then the Nightingale flew away. The attendants came in to see after their dead Emperor, and there he stood, bidding them: "Good morning!"

Lost in the Apple Cave

by CAROLYN SHERWIN BAILEY

illustrated by NINON

Swinging her worn shoes from the steps of the covered wagon whose great canvas top had been her only roof for months, Rose looked back along the wilderness road. At its beginning lay the mountains. Where the road ended was wide river. Rose and her father and mother were on their way from New England to that great unknown place beyond the Ohio River called the West. Everything they owned was packed in the great clumsy wagon, camped now on the banks of the Ohio until a flatboat should come to ferry it across. Rose had loved everything about the trip:

the slow movement along strange roads, the tinkle of bells on some peddler's mule, the glimpse of a passing wain full of barrels of maple syrup or of rawhides and raw wool, the evening's camp beside some brook with a supper of cornmeal mush and salt pork cooked over an open fire.

The big wagon was like home to the twelve-year-old girl. In a corner crowded with pewter plates, patchwork quilts, sacks of cornmeal, and gourds of milk, Rose had a family of dolls made of great pine cones she had gathered on the road. She had dressed them in bits of her own calico frock as it had become torn. The little heads of these dolls, made of small wild apples, wore sunbonnets like Rose's own, or hats made of plaited rushes gathered by the brooks. The pine-cone dolls had a set of dishes made of acorns.

Kicking her heels against the wagon step, feeling the warm harvest sun on her bare legs, Rose wished that she knew what lay within those deep woods at the right of their camp. She was sometimes lonely, for they had not happened to meet any other girl of her age all summer. She watched her mother bending over the knitting she was trying to finish before the sun dipped down into the river in flaming crimson. Her father was trying to catch some fish for supper. Rose stood up at last, swinging a little hand-made basket over her arm.

"I am going for a walk, Mother," she said. "Perhaps I can find some berries in the wood to eat with our porridge tonight."

"Do not go too far, Rose," her mother warned. "Your father saw a big brown bear quite close this morning."

"I will be back by suppertime," Rose said.

64

In five minutes from the time she left the wagon camp, Rose was out of all sight and sound of it. The faint stir of a passing snake among the fallen leaves in the forest, the rustle of a chipmunk's little feet, the flapping of a crow's wings or an owl's, were the only sounds. Rose hurried, remembering the bear. She never thought that she could lose the trail, but soon it seemed as if she were going round and round, each moment straying deeper into the wilderness. Her arms and legs were scratched by the bushes, each step was less sure. Rose ran. She clung to the little rush basket for comfort. It broke the force of her fall as she stepped down, tumbled, and found herself imprisoned in a cave. The entrance had been carefully screened by leafy boughs and bushes. When she got up and looked about, Rose could not believe her eyes.

The cave smelled deliciously of apples. Eating apples were a new fruit in those days, and rather rare. But here, in a roomy cave that had a little bubbling spring at the back to keep the fruit moist, was shelf upon shelf of wonderful apples such as Rose had never seen, stored away for the winter. There were August apples, the delight of harvesters. There were great golden pippins which made Rose think of the big bell on the church at home that had rung for their courage when the covered wagons started out; hard little russet apples that would keep all winter and be sweeter in March than they were now; and great red spicy apples, grown by grafting a shoot from a wild-apple bough into a bough of a sweet orchard-apple tree. Rose selected one of these apples and sat down in content on the mossy floor to munch it. This might be a bear's cave, she thought,

but it was the pleasantest place she had seen in a long time.

Bright skin, delicious juice, crunchy pulp, Rose ate her apple down to its nest of big black seeds. She was just cupping her hands to drink from the spring, when a shadow darkened the door of the cave. Could it be the bear of whom her mother had warned her? Rose was dumb with terror as she saw a dark form closing the cave entrance. But a voice reassured her.

"Don't be afraid, little girl. It's only Appleseed Johnny. Welcome to my orchard!"

The man, strange indeed with his long hair, ragged clothes, and feet bare save for Indian moccasins, held out his hand to Rose.

"Come and see my trees, little girl," he said. "Many of the people of the covered wagons make this orchard of mine their halfway house before they cross the Ohio River. Come and see my house, too, and then I will show you the way to the camp again."

As the man led Rose out of the cave and into a clearing where grew more apple, cherry, peach, and plum trees than she had ever seen before, he talked about himself. He was still a young man, but he said that he had traveled on foot to Pittsburgh all the long way—across mountains, fording streams, and breaking trails through the wilderness—from Springfield in Massachusetts. His name was John Chapman. He was called Appleseed Johnny because he was the only orchardman of the pioneers. He loved apples, and he knew how much the West needed fruit. The rich soil was fairly aching to nourish the seeds that he had begged from farmers in Pennsylvania and planted there on the banks of the Ohio River.

Appleseed Johnny showed Rose the shed where he sorted and washed apple seeds, started shoots for new trees, and kept his spade and pruning shears. Then they went into the big comfortable cabin he had built for himself of forest wood, lusty logs of oak, chestnut, and pine. An apple bough, gnarled and crooked into the shape of a forest gnome, was perched on the ridge of Appleseed Johnny's cabin for its rooftree. The nails that held the cedar planks of the door were handmade. So was the star-shaped iron latch that Appleseed Johnny lifted as he opened the heavy door and led Rose inside.

In the light of the big stone fireplace the girl thought that Appleseed Johnny looked like an Indian, as brown, sharp-eyed, and slender. He gave a low call, and down from a shelf near the roof fluttered a fluffy sleepy little owl and nestled on his shoulder.

"I came too far away from our wagon," Rose explained. "Folks say there are bears in these woods."

Appleseed Johnny laughed. He went to the door and made an odd growling sound. Fascinated, Rose saw a shaggy brown animal lumber out of the gathering darkness, sniff at Appleseed Johnny, and then pass by.

"All the wild creatures love this apple man," Rose thought.

Appleseed Johnny came in and filled a big pewter mug with milk for Rose. He put a comb of golden honey and three red apples in her basket. Last, he gave her a little apple tree, no taller than her pine-cone doll, and a small

deerskin bag of seeds.

"Now I will guide you to the edge of the woods," he said. "And when you come to your new home in the wilderness, set out this young apple tree in the sunshine, and water it, and build a little fence of brush about it to keep off the deer.

"In this bag are precious seeds of other apples, of berries, pears, cherries, grapes, plums, and peaches. Plant them and tend them, for there is no fruit in the wilderness. Your mother will want berries and fruits for her autumn pies, and jellies and preserves for the winter. Your new home in the West will need grapevines growing over it, and a pink cloud of orchard blossoms in the spring."

As Appleseed Johnny talked, he led Rose safely through the darkening forest until she could see her own campfire and smell the fish her mother was cooking.

"Goodbye, and thank you," she said.

"Goodbye, Little Pioneer," he said. "Remember Appleseed Johnny and plant your trees."

"I will!" she called as she ran over to hide her little tree and the seeds. She ate supper in a dream and in her sleep smelled apples under the canvas top. A flatboat was waiting for them in the morning, and they drifted, wagon and all, over the Ohio River and into the wild lands beyond.

Season after season Appleseed Johnny tended his trees, harvested his fruit, and sorted his seeds. He kept cows and had a row of beehives. Season after season the covered wagons carrying hundreds of pioneers West stopped by his cabin. The travelers were fed apples, honey, and milk and given little bags of Appleseed Johnny's precious seeds.

Rose's covered wagon rolled on into the untilled, wild country of Ohio. Her father told her about Appleseed Johnny. "He was only a boy when he left his home in Massachusetts and tramped out to Pennsylvania," he said. "He took apple seeds in payment for work for the farmers, and he built his house and planted his orchards with his own hands. Hundreds of covered wagons stop at his door, rest, and go on, carrying his bags of seeds."

On, on went the wagon until Rose's father found a farm site. The seasons passed quickly, with so much work to be done. The land was cleared and a cabin built in two years. That was the year that Rose picked berries from the bushes that grew from Appleseed Johnny's seeds. In four years roads were built, the cabin made larger, and Rose's dresses were longer. That was the year that she picked peaches, cherries, and plums from the trees planted from Appleseed Johnny's seeds. In six years Rose was a young lady. It was another October, and the apples from the little tree that Appleseed Johnny had given her were harvested and waiting in the kitchen to be made into apple butter for the winter. Rose would trust no one but herself to do this.

In the sunny kitchen she had set out empty pans, tubs, sharp knives, and a great basket of juicy red apples. On linen thread, hanging from the beams of the kitchen, were strips of apples drying. The strong crane in the open fireplace held a brass kettle filled with pared apples, sweet and sour in proportion, the sweet ones at the bottom, with quinces and molasses added for flavor. She had put straw in the bottom of the kettle to keep the cooking apples

73

from burning. Rose would spend days preserving the apples for the winter. Down cellar, tubs of applesauce would freeze and keep through the winter as sweet as when it was made. The dried apples would be made into pies.

Rose stirred the apple butter, her back to the open door. Suddenly she heard a low call, like that of a little screech owl. She turned and saw a surprising figure.

The man was as tall and straight as an Indian, keen-eyed, and on his back he carried a great sack. He was as ragged as a beggar, his hair had grown to his shoulders and he wore Indian moccasins. He gave his bird call again, and smiled at Rose. "You have grown, my child," he said.

"Appleseed Johnny!" she cried.

"Yes, I am Appleseed Johnny, still planting orchards in the wilderness. I gave away my house, filled this sack with seeds, crossed the Ohio River in a dugout canoe, and have been wandering for many years, scattering seeds, and teaching the pioneers how to plant and tend orchards."

"Come in," Rose begged. "Spend the night with us, and let us feed you as you fed me when I was a covered-wagon girl. These are your apples that I am cooking. Your little tree lived, and every one of your seeds grew and gave us fruit."

An old letter tells us the rest of the story: how Appleseed Johnny, pioneer nurseryman of the early nineteenth century, spent the night in the Rice cabin, made welcome by Roselle Rice and her family who had passed his door many years before. Many covered-wagon children knew Appleseed Johnny, but Rose was the only one who wrote about him. In the morning he started on again. He carried a Bible in the sack with his seeds, and left one leaf of it with Rose. Then he tramped off into the woods farther West and she never saw him again.

But Appleseed Johnny walked for forty years, leaving his little buckskin bags of seeds and his Bible pages at lonely cabins, planting the orchards that now cover acres of the West, sleeping outdoors, making friends with bears, wolves, and foxes, looked upon by the Indians as the Great Spirit. Pioneers went on with his work. Today skilled orchardmen cultivate the vast tracts of fruitland of our West. Following the trail he started, great freight trains return now to the East carrying barrels of Jonathan, Winesap, Spitzenburgh, Northern Spy, Delicious, King, Greening, and Golden Pippin apples for hungry boys and girls. The wild hardy stock poured into the spiced sap of the cultivated growth still gives us new, larger, tastier apples. The sturdy covered-wagon people, going West, gave us our beautiful Western cities, our fertile farms, our fine schools. And every pink apple blossom of the spring is scented with Appleseed Johnny's kindness to little Rose, and every bite of a rosy October apple tastes as sweet as those he laid away in his cave.

The Cow Who Fell
in the Canal

by PHYLLIS KRASILOVSKY

illustrated by PETER SPIER

Hendrika was an unhappy cow. She lived on a farm in Holland, where it is very flat. All summer long she ate grass. All winter long she ate hay. All winter and all summer she did nothing but eat.

And she gave milk to Mr. Hofstra, the farmer. Mr. Hofstra thought she was a fine cow because she gave such white creamy milk.

"Eat, eat, Hendrika," he would say. "The more you eat the more creamy white milk you can give me." Hendrika loved Mr. Hofstra, so she ate more to please him.

But she was unhappy.

77

In front of the pasture was a road. Every day Pieter, the horse, came with a wagon to take Hendrika's milk to the city. Pieter told Hendrika about the city.

"The streets are made of cobblestones and the houses have staircases on their roofs. People ride bicycles," he said.

Hendrika wanted to see the wonderful things Pieter talked about. She was tired of looking at Mr. Hofstra's house, the barn, and the windmill. The windmill wore a little porch. It went round and round in the wind. It made Hendrika dizzy.

78

In back of the pasture was a narrow canal. In the summertime a man came through the canal with a boat to take Mr. Hofstra's cheese to market. Hendrika liked the boats. She thought it would be nice to ride in a boat to market. Pieter said the cheese sellers wore colored straw hats with ribbons. Hendrika thought a colored hat would taste so so good!

Poor unhappy Hendrika! She longed to see something besides the house, the barn, and the windmill. Instead, she ate and ate and ate. And she grew fat, and then fatter, and then very very very fat. She grew so fat she could hardly move. She grew so fat she could hardly see!

79

One day she went farther and farther along the pasture.
She looked neither right nor left for she had eyes only for
the sweet grass, and before she knew it SHE FELL IN
THE CANAL!

The canal was not deep but it was deep enough for
Hendrika to get all wet. She was too fat to climb out so
she just stood in the water and ate the grass along the
bank. Mr. Hofstra didn't know that Hendrika was in the
canal, because he was busy getting his cheese ready for
market.

Hendrika was in the canal a long time. She ate so much
grass that she became sleepy. But she couldn't sleep in the
water. If only she could get back to the pasture! It was
springtime and there were flowers to eat! She walked and

walked along the edge of the canal eating grass when suddenly. . . .

She came upon an old raft! She pushed and pushed, and finally she fell on the raft and it drifted away from the bank.

HENDRIKA WENT FLOATING DOWN THE CANAL!

Past the pasture went Hendrika. Past the barn, the house, and the windmill. Past the tulips. Past the neighbor's barn, house, and windmill. Past more tulips. Past another barn.

Another house. Another windmill. Still more tulips. And still another windmill. Now Hendrika wasn't too sleepy to open her eyes. There was so much to see on both sides of the canal!

81

A whole row of houses with stair-cased roofs passed by.
Then some children on bicycles. "Look at the cow on the
canal!" they cried, and followed after on the road above
the canal.

Another row of stair-cased roofs passed by. Housewives
were cleaning windows and scrubbing doorsteps. They
laughed to see Hendrika floating along. They too followed
along the banks, laughing and exclaiming.

Soon a whole flock of people were running, walking, or
riding along the bank following the raft in the canal.

Hendrika loved all the attention she was getting. She mooed with happiness.

Suddenly the raft stopped and two boys pulled Hendrika to shore with a rope. Hendrika broke away and ran down the street.

It was hard to run on the cobblestones but Hendrika was enjoying the city at last.

On and on through the streets she went, with all the people following her.

She looked into windows and pranced into yards. She sniffed the bicycles. There was so much to see!

Just as Hendrika began to get a little tired she arrived at a big square. Here were whole crowds of people. Here were men wearing colored straw hats with streamers. Here were balls of cheeses piled high.

The market was just as Pieter told her it would be. And the blue straw hat tasted just as good as she thought it would!

Mr. Hofstra was there selling his cheeses, too. "Hendrika!" he cried when he saw her. "I thought you were home in the pasture eating grass, not here eating hats! A hat is to wear."

He was so surprised. Everyone laughed at his bewilderment.

Mr. Hofstra pushed Hendrika into Pieter's wagon and drove her home.

After that day Mr. Hofstra made certain that Hendrika was safe in the pasture. Hendrika didn't mind. Now she had so much to think about as she chewed the grass, looking so pretty in a colored straw hat with streamers!

The True Book of Space

by ILLA PODENDORF

illustrated by RICHARD SCARRY

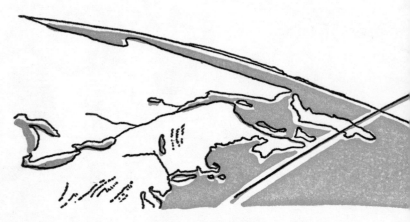

WHAT IS A SATELLITE?

The earth has a satellite that is called the moon. A satellite is a follower. It follows something bigger and greater than it is.

A prince may have his satellites. A prince's satellites are the people who follow him.

The moon follows the earth as the earth travels around the sun. The moon moves around the earth in a path called an orbit. The moon stays in its orbit because the pull of the earth keeps it there.

Rockets have sent man-made satellites into the sky. They

go around the earth in orbits of their own. The paths of the man-made satellites are between the earth and the orbit of the moon.

Animals were sent up in early man-made satellite flights. Instruments in satellites send back messages about space and about the sun and how it affects the earth.

Many questions had to be answered before scientists could send a satellite into space.

The world now knows that human beings can travel into faraway space.

Space scientists are working hard to answer many more questions before people travel regularly in faraway space.

WHERE IS SPACE?

When we look down a street, we look into space.

When we look across a field, we look into space.

When we look down a canyon, we look into space.

When we look into the sky, we look into space.

The sky is the biggest space that we know anything about.

We may see airplanes and clouds in the sky. But much of the space in the sky seems to have nothing in it.

All of these spaces around us are important in one way.

They all have air in them. There is air on the table, and air on the floor. There is air in every crack and hole on this earth. There is air in the ground and in the water.

When we look into the sky, we look into air. We cannot see air. Air has no color. We can feel air when the wind blows because wind is moving air.

There is air inside of us, too. When we take a deep breath, we take air into the little spaces in our lungs. We cannot live without air.

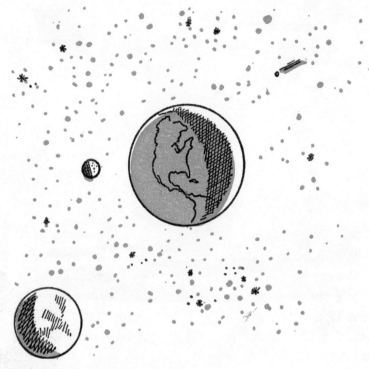

WHAT IS OUTER SPACE?

There is a faraway space.

It stretches out in all directions beyond the earth.

This space probably has very little in it. It has no air of the kind we know.

This faraway space is so big that a trip into it would last longer than we can imagine, if we traveled at the speeds we know on earth.

No one knows how far away this space goes. Scientists call it OUTER SPACE.

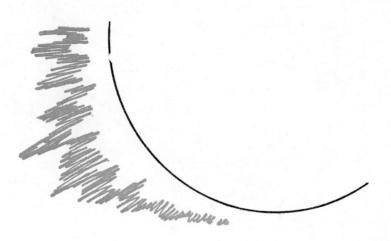

We can see some things in outer space.

We can see the moon, sun, planets and faraway stars.

We can see a meteor when it comes into the earth's air. It is a piece of a kind of rock from outer space. It burns up from heat made by rubbing against bits of air. We call it a "shooting star."

The moon is closer to the earth than the sun or any of the planets.

Some of the planets are closer to the earth than the sun is.

Some planets are farther from the earth than the sun is.

The stars are much farther away than the moon, the sun and the planets.

Outer space seems to have no end to it.

It is easy to understand that the space close to the earth which has air in it is much smaller than the faraway outer space.

HOW DO WE TRAVEL IN AIR THAT HAS SPACE IN IT?

There are many ways to travel in space which has air in it.

Scientists keep finding better ways for us to travel.

They invented the steam engine and people began to travel in boats and trains.

A few years later, scientists invented the gasoline engine. Only a little more than fifty years ago, the first automobile with a gasoline engine was made.

Scientists have made gasoline engines better and better. Now cars can go more than a mile a minute.

Some engines can burn other fuels besides gasoline. Some truck and bus engines burn oil.

But all of these engines must have oxygen from the air to help the fuels to burn.

For a long time, scientists have known how to build an airplane. But the gasoline engine made it possible to build one that had power enough to fly.

Now airplanes go much faster than cars. People travel in them every day. Helicopters are useful for short trips.

Jet planes do not work in the same way that planes with gasoline engines and propellers work. But they, too, must have oxygen to burn their fuels.

All planes need air to give oxygen to the motors. They also need air, flowing over the wings, to hold them up.

The air that we travel through in trains, cars, boats and planes is close to the earth.

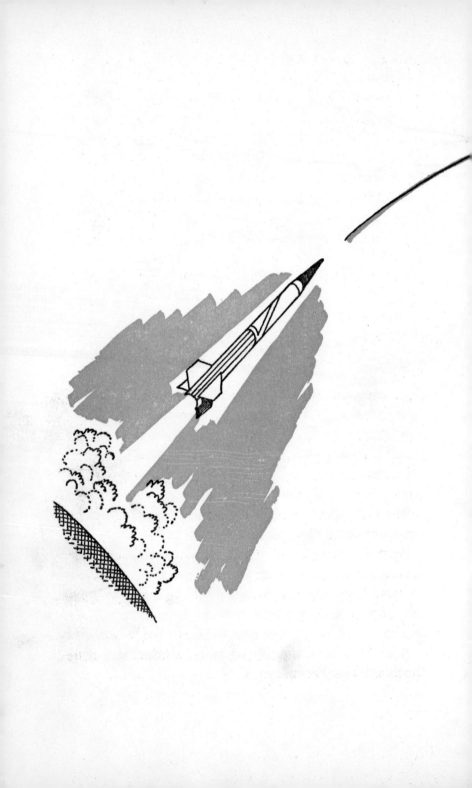

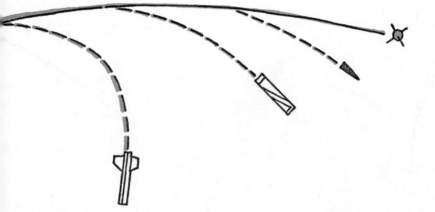

HOW DO ROCKETS TRAVEL IN OUTER SPACE?

Scientists are working hard to find a safe way to travel in outer space—space which does not have air in it.

A rocket has been invented which can go into outer space. A rocket carries its own oxygen and fuel with it.

Rocket ships can travel several miles in one second. This is much faster than a jet plane can go.

But when a rocket ship runs out of fuel or oxygen in outer space, there is no way to get more.

Scientists have made one, two, three, and four stage rockets.

One of the rockets starts the ship into space. When it runs out of fuel, it falls away.

The second rocket takes over and sends the ship farther.

After the second rocket falls away, the third one sends the ship still farther, and so on.

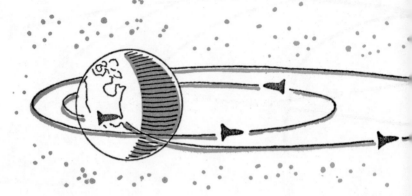

Once a rocket is beyond the air of the earth, it can keep going without any fuel.

There is no air to push against it and to slow down its speed. It may move into an orbit and circle the earth. It may become a satellite.

Instruments in satellites have sent messages back to earth.

Scientists have learned many things about outer space.

Scientists have learned that the sun's rays make things very hot in some parts of outer space.

Scientists have found out that things can be very cold in some parts of outer space.

They have learned that it is very dark in outer space.

They have learned that the sun's rays can be dangerous in outer space.

They have learned that outer space is silent—a place without sound.

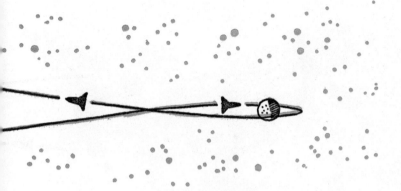

WHEN CAN WE TRAVEL IN OUTER SPACE?

Many things have been done in the last fifty years. But scientists have much more to do before most people can travel safely in outer space.

Large space ships must be made to go into outer space and to come safely back to earth.

When a rocket ship comes into the air from outer space, it is going very fast. It rubs against tiny bits of air, which could make the ship so hot it could melt or burn.

Scientists have been developing new materials and heat shields to protect rockets and space ships from the dangers of burning or melting.

They have also found good ways to slow down a space ship as it returns into the air. With less speed, the ship will not burn or melt.

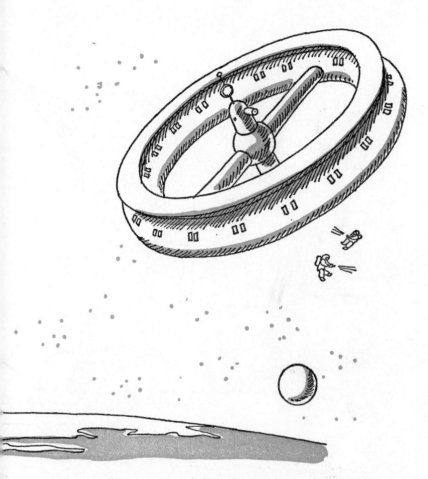

A space station or platform may some day be built out in space.

Space ships or rockets may get more fuel at the space station.

Space ships might be built or put together at the space station.

Scientists may find new fuels for space travel. They are trying to find a way to use atomic energy in space ships. Some day scientists may use power from the sun for space travel.

A way must be found to guide a space ship so that it will not be hit by a meteor while it is going through space.

People in space ships must have air to breathe and air around their bodies all the time. Special suits must be worn to protect people from dangerous rays from the sun.

Every day scientists learn more about outer space. They have found answers to many problems of safe travel in space. But they are working on many more of them.

Some scientists think that all of the problems will take a long time to overcome.

Other scientists believe that the most important problems will be solved in a few years, and that many more people can then travel safely in outer space.

The time may come when we will know much more about traveling at great speed, using better fuels, building more powerful rockets, getting air and food while we travel, and returning safely to earth.

That will be the time when you and I can travel in and out of outer space and tell about the trip.

Wee Brigit O'Toole

by RUTH AND RICHARD HOLBERG

illustrated by POLLY JACKSON

One winter morning Wee Brigit O'Toole woke up and found so much snow had fallen that Orchard Street was filled deep with it. As Brigit hustled into her long-legged underwear and hitched her long, black stockings over her cold, red knees, Mrs. O'Toole said, "Sure and ye can't go to school today at all, at all. There'll not be a gossoon there wid all this snow."

Wee Brigit, her older sister, Margaret Mavourneen, and her brother, Terry, ran to the kitchen window to look out.

"Oh, see!" cried Wee Brigit. "Mitty is on her back steps filling a bucket with snow!"

"I know why!" said Margaret Mavourneen importantly because she was the oldest and Mitty was her best friend. "Mitty is going to help her mother because it is Friday Sweeping Day."

Wee Brigit and Terry looked surprised and wondered what a bucket of snow had to do with Sweeping Day.

So Margaret Mavourneen said, "Mitty's mother sprinkles it on the Brussels carpet in their parlor and then sweeps it all up and the dust comes with it."

"Oh!" said Wee Brigit, nodding her curly head wisely. "Then when Mitty dusts the chairs and tables there isn't so much dust on them because it didn't fly up—the snow kept it down!"

Just then some jolly-sounding sleigh bells came jingling down the street, and the next thing there was Mr. Syrup, the Milkman, ringing his hand bell, "Cling, clang! Cling, clang!"

"Here comes Mr. Syrup!" shouted Wee Brigit.

The twins in the baby buggy, Tommy Patrick and Dennis Duffy, kicked and crowed and blew bubbles all over their clean bibs because they were glad to hear the bells.

Mr. Syrup opened the back door and a cold, sweet wind came in with him. He was saying in a loud voice, "Tomorrow we are going to have a sleigh-ride party out to my farm! Who wants to come?"

"Oh, please can I go? I'm big enough now!" Wee Brigit danced around him while Margaret Mavourneen held the pitcher for milk and Terry joggled the twins to make them laugh harder. Wee Brigit had always been too small to go on picnics or sleigh rides without her mother, but now she was seven.

"Indeed you can, Wee Brigit," said Mr. Syrup. "I have been inviting children all morning. Everyone is home from school because of the deep snow. Tomorrow I will stop right after dinner with the big bobsled for you!" And he rattled the top of the milkcan and was off next door to tell Mitty.

As soon as Mitty finished dusting she put on her coat and hood and overshoes, and ran to the O'Tooles to talk about the sleigh-ride party.

Wee Brigit and Margaret Mavourneen were playing house. Their mother's shawl was spread over two chairs and they sat under it with their dolls. Terry had the kitchen table upside down and he was playing boat.

Mrs. O'Toole said to Mitty, "Sure and it's a fine party that Mr. Syrup is after giving ye. I'm that busy washing and ironing clothes for the girls, and Terry needs another patch to his pants."

"I'm so glad we are all going," said Mitty. Just as she was crawling under the shawl to play, Wee Brigit pulled her aside and whispered something in her ear. Mitty never laughed at Wee Brigit's ideas as Margaret Mavourneen did sometimes when she remembered to be a big sister. And this time Mitty listened with big eyes, and nodded her head wisely.

"Oh, that will be fun," she giggled, and then they both went to see Mrs. Johnson, the Norwegian dressmaker who lived on the other side of Mitty's house. Mrs. Johnson was tripping lightly around her house with a little shovel. There was a live coal covered with ground coffee on it, and it made a nice spicy smell.

"What are you doing, Mrs. Johnson?" both girls asked at once.

"I'm trying to get rid of the strong smell of Lutfisk because my best customer is coming!"

Wee Brigit wrinkled up her freckled nose and sniffed. "Smells good now, not a bit like fish. But we came to tell you about the sleigh-ride party."

"OH MY!" said Mrs. Johnson.

"We want to whisper something to you," Wee Brigit giggled.

They put their heads together for quite a while. Mrs. Johnson nodded and smiled and went to a cupboard and brought back something and gave it to Wee Brigit, who thanked her very politely.

The next morning was Saturday. Wee Brigit watched at the front window all dressed up. She had a small package under her arm.

"Now mind ye blow your noses when ye should!" said Mrs. O'Toole, pinning clean handkerchiefs to their dresses. "And Terry, put on your best manners!"

All of a sudden the big bobsled came down the street and stopped. It was quite full of children. The O'Tooles and Mitty ran out and their mothers waved from the windows. The sled was filled with hay and there were buffalo robes to pull over. The hay smelled so sweet and Wee Brigit, cuddled down between Mitty and Margaret Mavourneen, was very excited. Mr. Syrup shouted "GID-DAP!" to the horses and they were off, going smooth and fast down the snowy streets.

Mr. Syrup had tin horns for the children to blow, and

the sleigh bells on the horses jingled a bright, merry sound.

Some of the boys tried to reach out for snowballs. Terry jumped off the end of the sled and filled his red mittens with snow. He ran after the sled but he couldn't catch it.

Wee Brigit watched him trying to catch up.

"Oh, Mr. Syrup!" she called. "Stop for Terry!"

Mr. Syrup only laughed and didn't stop.

Wee Brigit began to feel like crying.

"Oh, Mr. Syrup! PLEASE stop for Terry!"

Mr. Syrup stopped at last and Terry caught up and climbed in the sled all out of breath.

"Terry, don't do that again," begged Wee Brigit, her Irish blue eyes running over with tears.

Mr. Syrup said, "Don't do that again, Terry. Maybe the horses won't stop the next time."

Terry said he would never jump off again.

It was beginning to get a little cold and the children snuggled into the warm hay and sang school songs. After a while Mr. Syrup stopped at a little country store, shouting, "Whoa—Whoa . . .

"Jump out, we'll go in and get warmed up."

The village store was heated by a big round stove. Two men were playing checkers on a box. A cat was sleeping on the counter. The storekeeper was a long thin man with a big black mustache. He was rolling a sheet of brown paper into a cornucopia and he filled it with eggs and turned in the top neatly.

Everyone crowded around the warm stove.

Except Mr. Syrup. He took a cracker from a barrel and winked at Mr. Apple, the storekeeper. Then he drew the long knife sticking in a round yellow cheese and cut off a snip of cheese to eat with his cracker.

Soon everyone was warm and ready to start.

"Jingle, jingle, jingle," went the sleighbells on the horses. "Toot, toot, toot," went the tin horns as the children blew them with puffed-out red cheeks.

The snow was bright and the shadows of bare trees across the snow was blue. Red barns and farm houses with smoke curling from chimneys looked so cozy that Wee Brigit could not decide which was nicest, winter or summer. Then all of a sudden, they stopped. They were at Mr. Syrup's farm and there was his sister, Miss Lucy, standing at the kitchen window looking for them.

Yonny Yumper, the hired man, came from the barn to take the horses to their oats. The children tramped in the kitchen, stamping off the snow on the porch. There were so many wet mittens that Miss Lucy hung them on a line back of the stove to dry.

"Now," she said, "we are going to have a candy pull!"

The children gathered around and she put a big iron kettle on the stove and measured molasses and sugar and butter into it. They all took turns stirring it until Miss Lucy said, "Wee Brigit, fill up a cup with cold water."

When a drop of the boiling mixture made a hard lump in the water, Miss Lucy took it off the stove and poured the hot candy into a buttered pan.

"Now, Terry, you put that outside the back door to cool," she said.

Then she showed them how to pop corn. Some of the boys and girls shucked the corn from the cobs, others held the popper over the hot fire. Mr. Syrup went out and brought in more kindling wood for the fire. He told funny stories and sang Norwegian songs and danced funny steps that shook the floor. Miss Lucy looked worried at that, but she took Terry with her to look at the candy.

"Oh, it's just right now," she said.

She showed the children how to hold a piece of the candy with the tips of their fingers and thumbs and pull it. She and Terry pulled together.

Everybody wanted Mr. Syrup for a partner but Mitty said, "Wee Brigit O'Toole is his partner." They exchanged secret smiles and said, "Of course, of course, Wee Brigit O'Toole is his partner!"

The candy, that was dark brown when they began pulling it into a long rope, soon turned white. When it was just right, not too hard and not too soft, they cut the strips with scissors into pieces just big enough to eat, and spread them on buttered plates.

Mr. Syrup begged, "Let's play games while we eat our taffy and popcorn."

"Don't eat too much," warned Miss Lucy, "or you will spoil your appetites for supper. I'm going to let you take plenty home with you."

They played "I've come to see Miss Jenny Jones," and made a lot of noise. Then Miss Lucy noticed Wee Brigit whispering something to Mitty.

"Wee Brigit, have you got a secret?"

"Ssssh!" Wee Brigit put her finger on her lip and looked anxious. "I want to whisper something important to you, please."

"Come upstairs with me," Miss Lucy whispered.

Wee Brigit and Miss Lucy slipped out when no one was looking and the children were all singing loudly, "I've come to see Miss Jenny Jones and how is she today."

When they came down they were smiling and trying not to show it, and Miss Lucy said to Mr. Syrup, "Why don't you show the children the spare room where Mitty slept when she visited us last summer?"

But Mr. Syrup said, "I should think you would want me to show them the tree where I carved her name and the date!"

"OH NO!" she said and Wee Brigit looked worried. "The children don't want to put on coats and hats."

"Well—all right!" said Mr. Syrup, and he went upstairs

with all the children at his heels, all except Wee Brigit.

She went to her coat in the kitchen bedroom for the package she had brought with her. It was not there. It was not under her coat. It was not under anyone's coat. Her Irish blue eyes filled with tears and ran down over the black lashes.

"For pity's sake!" Miss Lucy cried. "Is it lost? What can have become of it?"

Wee Brigit threw herself on top of all the coats and cried hard.

"I remember putting it under my coat," she sobbed and

sobbed with sorrow.

Miss Lucy knelt down and tried to look under the bed. "My, my, what a lot of dust," she said sadly. "Wee Brigit, you crawl under and look, my knees are too stiff."

Wee Brigit blew her nose hard and crawled under. She reached her hand around but she did not find anything. She crawled on her stomach as far as the wall and reached out in the dark. She touched something. She clutched it hard and began to back out, bumping her head on the bed-springs.

Miss Lucy helped her up and brushed off the dust, saying, "There now, it wasn't lost after all. Hurry and let me wipe the smudges off your face and brush your curls first."

They hurried into the sitting room and none too soon, for Mr. Syrup and the children were coming downstairs.

They began to giggle and grin and push Mr. Syrup toward the center table. He looked around and stopped all of a sudden and said, "Why! There is a package all done up in pink tissue paper and white baby ribbons!"

He picked it up and opened it and looked.

"Why! It is a picture of school children! I wonder who they are?"

All the children looked at each other with long faces. Wee Brigit was almost ready to cry again.

Then all of a sudden he said, "Why bless my soul! If it isn't a picture of Wee Brigit's school. There she is herself, the blessed image of her dear mither, curls and freckles and all!"

Mitty's pigtails bobbed with excitement.

"Here I am next to Wee Brigit!" she cried.

Margaret Mavourneen pointed with a sticky finger. "Here I am!"

"Here I am!" shouted Terry O'Toole.

All the children showed Mr. Syrup just where they were on the photograph and they told him Wee Brigit thought of giving him the picture all by herself.

"Well, well!" he said. "This is the biggest and best surprise I ever had in my life. And such pretty tissue paper and ribbons all around it!"

Wee Brigit piped up, "Mrs. Johnson gave us the paper and baby ribbon because Mitty comes to see her every Sunday."

"But it was Wee Brigit's idea," said Mitty. "She wanted to make a pretty package."

Just then Miss Lucy called, "Come to supper!"

They had such a good supper with hot creamy cocoa and fresh farm bread and butter. There was summer sausage and dried beef and Wisconsin brick cheese. There was raspberry jam, cookies, spice cake and strawberry sauce.

Yonny Yumper came to the door and when Mr. Syrup saw him he shouted, "It's time to go home. Get your coats and hats and hoods on!

"And here is a buffalo robe for my partner, Wee Brigit O'Toole! She's going to ride in front with me."

Then the sleigh bells jingled and the sled flew over the hard snow and the sky was dark blue.

Wee Brigit was warm and cosy beside Mr. Syrup.

"Didn't we have fun!" said Wee Brigit.

"Yes we did," said Mr. Syrup. "And I'll always keep the picture of my partner and the other children forever!"

Chimpanzees are playful.

Pets Around the World

Hundreds of different animals are kept as pets in various parts of the world. The biggest one is the Elephant. One

Baby Lion works on Daddy's slipper.

of the smallest is the Cricket. In China, believe it or not, people make pets of Crickets because they like to hear them chirp!

The Chimpanzee is one of the most famous pets. He is so smart that he can be taught many tricks. He often learns to wear fancy clothes and ride a bicycle. He will even learn to sew on buttons and tie bowknots. And he has one of the funniest faces in the whole world.

Most baby Lions are as safe and playful as pet kittens while they are still little fellows. The one in the picture is having a wonderful time with an old slipper. As he grows older he will become very large and powerful. Then he will have to be kept in a cage at the zoo. This is because he might hurt somebody very badly.

Regular kittens are much better pets. They never seem to get tired of playing, and they are not dangerous when they grow up. These are some of the reasons why millions of people have them as pets.

Our pet Cats of today began as wild animals. That was a very long time ago. Their original ancestors are called Civets. Civets still live in Egypt. You can see one of them in the photograph.

The ancient Egyptians caught these Civets and made pets of them. Some people still do this today.

The real home of the queer-looking Mac Lemur is among the rocks in Madagascar, a big island in the Indian Ocean. This Lemur is something like a monkey. You can tell this from the shape of his feet. Years ago he was quite common, but today he is rare.

The Mac Lemur is known as a one-person pet. That is,

The Cat, early friend of man

he picks out some particular person as a friend. He can live in almost any climate. And he will not wander away from the house.

The Civet—original "cat"

The Mac Lemur

Man's oldest friend   *Docile Cheetah*

Our largest four-legged friend is the Asiatic Elephant. He has helped and worked with people for thousands of years. Most of the time he is friendly, gentle and patient. You would not like to buy food for this pet, as he eats seven hundred pounds a day.

An Elephant has a lot of sense, and can be trained to do many useful things. For example, he will pile big logs together or haul a truck out of the mud. You have probably seen him do astonishing circus tricks. When he has learned something, he never forgets it.

A Cheetah looks somewhat like a huge spotted cat with long legs. But he is not a real cat. He behaves more like a dog, and he has dog-like toenails.

The Cheetah can run at least as fast as seventy miles an hour. In his native East Africa he is trained to chase and catch other large animals which are less speedy. With people, though, he is surprisingly gentle. The one in the picture will take a walk with his owner and behave himself

Mongooses are "ratters."   *Capybara, "seeing-eye" pet*

perfectly. Furthermore, unlike his cousin the tiger, the Cheetah is very quiet-voiced, and greets his friends with a restful purr.

There are several kinds of Mongooses in the world. But only two of them have become family pets. These two are from India. They become very tame and make first-rate pets. In their native country they spend most of their time in the house or close to it, and are most interested in all the activities of the household. These playful creatures love to snatch bright objects off tables and scamper away with them. If a Mongoose finds a rat or a snake he will kill it. No wonder the family likes to have him around!

Another favorite tropical pet is the queer-looking Capy-bara, of South America. He is something like a giant guinea pig. His natural home is near rivers, but he is gentle and easily tamed. He is sometimes trained to lead a blind person, the way "seeing-eye dogs" do in our own country.

The Ferret, a friend of many European children

Over in Europe the gray, brown and black Polecat, or Ferret, often becomes a splendid children's pet. Of course he is not a cat at all. He really belongs to the weasel tribe.

The clever Kinkajou

Capuchin Monkey

These Ferrets are often used in Europe to catch rabbits. This is against the law in America. So, if you want to have a Ferret as a pet, you must get a license for him and keep him under control.

The brown, long-tailed Kinkajou, from the American tropics, is really amazing. He is related to our own raccoon, but he can hang by his tail like an opossum. He can use his front paws, or hands, as skillfully as any monkey.

Lots of people have kept Kinkajous as pets. They certainly are amusing fellows. But they do have sharp claws which can make plenty of trouble.

Right next to the Kinkajou picture you will see a Capuchin Monkey. He comes from tropical America, too. There are several varieties of this monkey. All of them have been popular pets for many years.

You never can tell what a pet Capuchin will do next. He may be as good as gold for ten minutes. Then he suddenly takes off around the room like a whirlwind. If you are patient you can teach him funny tricks. He will never forget them. But that does not mean that he will always obey you!

Tame bunnies come in dozens of colors and sizes. Some have long hair and others short fur. There are kinds with stand-up ears and different kinds with floppy ones. All of them are easy to keep and feed. They are all gentle, too, except sometimes the old males.

Bunnies, or Rabbits, have been favorite pets all over the world for thousands of years.

Baby Chicks are jolly little pets, too. The only trouble with them is that they grow up so quickly!

Domestic "Bunny" Rabbit   *Chicks—good farm pets*

And of course there are many kinds of Dogs. They have been marvelous pets and helpers for a very long time. No wonder that we call them our best animal friends.

Beagle puppies are very appealing.

Little Eddie, Junk Collector

by CAROLYN HAYWOOD

illustrated by ROBERT MACLEAN

Never a week went by without Eddie bringing home some piece of what Eddie called "valuable property," and his father called "junk."

The family always knew when Eddie had brought home a new treasure. Eddie would always announce at dinner, "I had a very enjoyable day today." When Eddie said this, his father would look at his mother and say, "Uh! Oh!"

After dinner his father would go down to the basement, and there he would find another piece of junk added to Eddie's collection.

"Now, see here, Edward!" said his father one evening. "This junk collecting has reached the limit. What happens every week? I'll tell you. On Friday night every man in this neighborhood puts his rubbish out for the rubbish collectors, and every Saturday a large part of it lands in our basement. Now, I am tired of it. The basement looks like a junk shop, or worse. It looks like a dump. We will never get all of this stuff out of the basement."

"But, Papa!" said Eddie. "I don't want it out. It's my valuable property."

"Valuable property!" exclaimed his father. "Junk! Nothing you ever bring home is worth the room it takes."

The following Saturday Rudy and the twins went on a hike with some of the boys in Rudy's class in school. Eddie wanted to go, too, but they said that he was too little. He felt very badly until his mother said that he could go for a drive in the car with herself and his father. They were going out into the country to see if they could find a shop where they could buy a nice tilt-top table.

It was a beautiful day, and as they drove along the roads Eddie saw the cows and the horses on the farms. He saw men working in the fields. He read the signs along the road. *Fresh Eggs. Broilers.*

The first time Eddie saw the word "broiler," he said, "What is a broiler?"

"It's a young chicken that is small enough to broil," said his mother.

Eddie could read most of the billboards. He found it exciting to be able to read, to have letters mean something.

They had been driving for about an hour when Mr. Wilson brought the car to a stop in front of a store. There was a large sign hanging outside which Eddie could not read. "What does that sign say, Pop?" asked Eddie.

"It says *Antiques*," said his father.

"Are we going to see Aunt Teek?" asked Eddie. "Does she own the store?"

"Not Aunt Teek," said his father. "Antiques. Antique means old. When you see that sign, it means that the shop sells old things."

"You mean junk?" said Eddie. "Sounds exciting!"

"No, indeed!" said his father. "These things are valuable."

By this time, Mr. and Mrs. Wilson and Eddie had gotten out of the car. They walked up the path to the porch.

"I never saw a store with a porch before," said Eddie.

"Well, you're in the country now," said his mother. "They often have porches."

Eddie looked around the porch. It was full of all kinds of objects. Among them were some huge kettles, some fire screens, and brass and iron andirons. There were long iron

forks and tongs for handling the logs in a fireplace. There was an old wooden bench, and a big wooden box with pictures painted on it.

"Gee!" said Eddie. "It sure looks like junk."

The windows of the shop were filled with shelves, and the shelves were covered with glass vases, cups, plates, salt-cellars, pitchers, and sugar bowls.

The inside of the store was crammed with furniture—tables, chairs, chests of drawers, and cabinets full of china. The store was big. It seemed to Eddie to go back, and back, and back.

"Jeepers!" thought Eddie. "I'll bet a fellow could find some very valuable property around here."

While his father and mother were busy talking to the owner of the shop, Eddie wandered toward the back of the place. He looked over the shelves; he peered into open boxes and barrels. Finally he went through a doorway into what seemed to be a storeroom. There he came upon a man opening a barrel.

"Hello, son!" said the man. "Can I do something for you?"

"I'm just looking around," said Eddie. "My father and mother are out there." Eddie pointed to the front of the store.

In a moment Eddie's eyes fell upon something that interested him very much indeed. On a shelf stood an old carriage lamp. It was rusty and covered with dust.

"Do you want to sell that lamp?" Eddie asked the man who was opening the barrel.

The man looked up. "I guess we do," he replied.

"How much is it?" asked Eddie.

"Oh, 'bout a quarter," said the man.

Eddie reached into his pocket and pulled out all of his money. He had seventy-five cents. Twenty-five cents was his weekly allowance. His father had given it to him that morning. The other fifty cents he had earned during the week, delivering orders for Mr. Henderson. His regular boy was away.

"Okay!" said Eddie. "I'll take it."

The man took the lamp from the shelf and blew the dust off of it. "Want it wrapped up?" he asked.

Just then Eddie's eye fell upon another interesting object. It had been hidden behind the carriage lamp. "What is that?" asked Eddie, pointing to what looked like a small iron urn with a wheel on each side. It, too, was rusty.

"Oh, that?" asked the man, lifting it down. "That's an old-fashioned coffee grinder."

"Those wheels are super!" said Eddie, his eyes very big.

"How much is that?"

"Oh, I guess I can let you have that for fifty cents," said the man.

Eddie looked at the coffee grinder for a few moments. Then he said, "I'll take that, too."

"Want them wrapped?" asked the man.

"Yes, please," replied Eddie, taking a look out to the front of the store. His mother and father were busy looking at some dishes.

"Suppose I put them in this carton," said the man.

"That will be fine," said Eddie.

Eddie watched the man put the coffee grinder into the bottom of the carton. Then he put the lamp on top. When he folded over the flaps, they didn't close because the end of the lamp was too long. The man tied a piece of cord over the top to hold the flaps down, but the end of the lamp still showed. "I guess that will do," he said.

"Oh, sure!" replied Eddie, as he handed over his seventy-five cents. "That will do."

Eddie decided to go out of the back door with his package. Once outside, he ran to the car. He thought it would be best to put the package in the trunk of the car. His father had left the keys in the car, so Eddie unlocked the trunk and placed the package on the shelf. Then he locked the trunk and put the keys in his pocket.

Eddie sauntered back to the front porch. He was examining a broken lock when his father and mother came out.

"Look, Papa," said Eddie. "This is a swell lock."

"It's a piece of junk," said Mr. Wilson. "No more junk is going into our house, Eddie. Put it down."

Eddie put the lock down and walked to the car with his father and mother. "You left the keys in the car, Pop," said Eddie, handing over the bunch of keys.

"Oh, thanks, Eddie," said his father.

They all climbed into the car. Eddie sat between his father and mother.

"Didn't they have any table, Mother?" asked Eddie.

"No, dear," replied Mrs. Wilson. "But they expect one in next week."

For some time they drove in silence. Then suddenly Eddie said, "Well, I had a very enjoyable time."

Mr. and Mrs. Wilson immediately looked down at Eddie. He looked up at them with a sweet smile on his face. Then they looked at each other. Mr. Wilson put on the brakes and stopped the car. He turned around and looked on the back seat of the car and on the floor. There was nothing there.

"What did you say, Eddie?" his father asked.

Eddie looked up and said, "I just said I've had a very enjoyable time."

Mr. Wilson took the keys from the car, opened the door, and stepped out. He walked around to the back of the car, opened the trunk, and there was Eddie's package.

Eddie, standing beside his father, said, "Please, Papa, it isn't junk. It's swell stuff."

"Eddie!" said his father, "when I said, 'No more junk,' I meant it. This isn't going another foot of the way home." To Eddie's amazement, his father placed the package in a ditch beside the road.

As Mr. Wilson leaned over, he saw the end of the carriage lamp sticking out of the top of the carton. He pulled off the cord, and lifted the lamp out of the carton.

"Say!" he cried. "Why, this is a carriage lamp. Say! This is mine. Why, I have been wanting one of these for a long time. I want it to go on the post at the front gate. Why, this is a beautiful carriage lamp. It just needs to be refinished. Well, now! This is mine!"

"But I bought it, Papa," said Eddie. "I paid for it."

"Well, I'll give you a dollar for it, Eddie," said his father. "How is that?"

"Okay!" said Eddie.

In the midst of this discovery, Mrs. Wilson joined Eddie and his father.

"Look, Mother!" Mr. Wilson cried. "Look at this fine carriage lamp. This is mine."

Mrs. Wilson was busy looking into the carton which still lay in the ditch. "Why, look at this old coffee grinder!" she cried. "Oh! What a duckie coffee grinder! Oh, this is mine! These old coffee grinders make the most beautiful lamps you ever saw! Mrs. Porter has one, and it's lovely. With a coat of red paint, this will be perfect."

Mrs. Wilson held the old coffee grinder very lovingly. "Oh! This is mine!" she said.

"But I bought it, Mamma," said Eddie. "I paid for it."

"Oh, well. I'll give you a dollar for it," said his mother. "Is a dollar all right?"

"Ah, Mamma!" said Eddie. "I like that coffee grinder. I like it a lot."

"Well, I'll give you two dollars for it," said his mother. "That's a lot of money, Eddie. Think how rich you will be."

"Okay!" said Eddie.

The three went back to the car. Mr. Wilson went first, carrying his carriage lamp. Then Mrs. Wilson, carrying her coffee grinder. Little Eddie brought up the rear, with three dollars in his small fist.

When they were almost home, Mr. Wilson said, "By

the way, Eddie, how much did you pay for that lamp?"

"A quarter," said Eddie.

"And how much did you pay for the coffee grinder?" asked his father.

"Fifty cents," Eddie replied.

"Not bad!" said his father, looking at his mother.

"You know, Papa!" said Eddie. "I've been thinking. Do you know what I'm going to be when I grow up?"

"No," replied Mr. Wilson. "What are you going to be?"

"I'm going to be a junk man," said Eddie. "That's a good way to get rich."

"How about letting me go into business with you?" asked his father.

"Okay, Papa!" said Eddie. "Will we have a store?"

"Oh, certainly!" said his father. "And we'll have a big sign that says, *Wilson and Son—All Kinds of Junk.*"

The Man in the Manhole and The Fix-it Men

by JUNIPER SAGE

illustrated by EARL THOLLANDER

Fix it, fix it, where are the Fix-it Men?
Down in the ground in a dark manhole,
Or up in the air on a telephone pole.
Fix it, fix it, here come the Fix-it Men.

No one was on the street. It was a big empty quiet street with long morning shadows.

There was a silent sign on the empty street that said MEN AT WORK.

But there were no men in sight, not even a cat.

And everything was quiet and very still, not a sound, not even a smell.

When suddenly . . .

Up popped a man out of a manhole.

He had a blue handkerchief around his neck, and a big hooked crowbar in one hand, and a big monkey wrench in the other. And he walked down the street until he came to the other manhole. He took his big crowbar and pried up the manhole lid. Then he leaned down the hole and shouted, "Ho, Joe!"

The echo came back, *Ho, Joe.*

Then from far away in the darkness a smaller voice hollered back, "Ho, Tonio." *Ho, Tonio.*

Tonio went climbing down the pipe tunnel. It was a big dark tunnel under the street, big enough for a fat man to walk through without squeezing.

Tonio followed the little pipe running through the tunnel, till he came splashing into the water.

A joint was loose in the little pipe.

So Tonio whipped out his monkey wrench and wrenched up the leak.

"That fixes it," said Tonio.

Up in the air the wind began to blow. And it blew the wires down.

> Fix it, fix it, here come the Fix-it Men.
> Down in the ground in a dark manhole,
> Or up in the air on a telephone pole.
> Fix it, fix it, here come the Fix-it Men.

The Telephone Man arrived in a black hat with a coil of wire over his shoulder. He climbed up the pole. He had spikes on the heels of his shoes that stuck in the wooden pole.

When he got to the top he buckled his belt around the pole. This kept him from falling.

The wires were humming close to his ear. He leaned back against his belt, took out his wire cutter, and cut off the broken wire. The old wire fell to the ground.

He put on the new wire. The wires began to hum again.
Birds flew past the telephone poles and some sparrows settled on the new wire.

"That fixes it," said the Telephone Man.

Down below the cars went up and down, up and down the road. And a street light flashed red, then green. Stop . . . Go . . . Stop . . . Go.

The shadows had grown shorter and the morning was almost gone.

But the Fix-it Men kept coming and going along the road.

The world kept breaking and having to be fixed and mended.

Everyone was busy.

SMASH! BANG!

There was a terrible smash and a bang. A big motor car and a little old taxi smashed in a terrible smash.

The drivers jumped out to see what had happened. They were mad and they growled at each other.

The motor car still looked shiny, but the poor little taxi

was all smashed up. The headlights were smashed, the bumper was smashed. The shiny paint was all scratched.

But what really mattered was the little old taxi couldn't run any more.

> *Fix it, fix it, here come the Fix-it Men.*
> *Men on four wheels to fix automobiles,*
> *Men with big loads to fix broken roads.*
> *Fix it, fix it, here come the Fix-it Men.*

Here comes the wrecking truck to pull the little wrecked taxi away.

The wrecking truck is small and strong and painted green with a crane out behind with a big black hook like a tail.

The truckman tried to start the taxi but the engine wouldn't roar. It wouldn't even make a noise.

The truckman scratched his head.

The truckman shrugged his shoulders.

"What a fix!" he said.

Then he hooked the hook around the bumper.

"That fixes it, and what a fix!"

And they pulled it away to fix it some more.

The road to the South was broken. It was a bumpy road.

Up went a big fence. Up went a red flag. Up went a lantern.

And up went a sign saying ROAD UNDER REPAIR, all across the road.

And coming down the street were road men with a cement mixer. They are going to make cement for the new road. They make the cement out of sand and water and powdered cement all mixed up together.

There were three men, three road menders. One poured in the water, one poured in the sand and cement, and one told the other two what to do. He was the Boss Man.

"Let her go!" shouted the Boss Man.

The little cement mixer whirled and churned. They pulled open the door and out came gray cement like glorious mud all over the road.

Then the next morning along came the tar wagon.

This dirty little wagon was full of tar. But the tar was as hard as coal until they melted it over a red hot fire in the belly of the wagon.

There was the smell of tar in the air.

Then they sloshed the black shiny tar all over the road.
They sprinkled yellow sand on top of it.

Woe to the bug or the frog or the barefoot boy who tried
to cross that road.

And the next day when the sunlight was still cool, S-s-s-
s-s-s-s-s. *Clunk-clunk-clunk.* Along came the steam roller
down the road.

The fire burned in the belly of the steam roller and
boiled the water that made the steam roller go. The great
round rollers went round and round, pushing down the tar,
flat as a shadow in the middle of the road. It rolled and
rolled until the road was smooth and flat and hard.

"That fixes it," said the Boss Man.

That fixes it!

Out in the country a house was broken. A hole in the roof let the rain in. A hole in the window let the wind in. A crack in the wall let the gray plaster show.

Something had to be done before more wind came through the window and more rain came through the roof and more grayness through the old wall.

> *Fix it, fix it, here come the Fix-it Men.*
> *Carpenters coming with hammers and nails,*
> *Painters arriving with paint in their pails.*
> *Fix it, fix it, here come the Fix-it Men.*

bang
bang
bing
a
dee
bang

The Carpenter climbed out of a window and up onto the roof. He had on carpenters' overalls with lots of pockets, and nails and rulers and a carpenter's square and a big flat pencil in his pocket.

Bang-bang-bing-a-dee-bang! He fixed the hole in the roof where the rain came in. And he fixed the hole where the wind came in.

All this time the Painter was slapping bright wet paint all over the walls inside the house.

And he slapped right over the gray spot till the whole room was bright and new.

He gave a final slap with his brush.

"That fixes it," he said.

The moon came down the night. All through the town the Fix-it Men were asleep in their own beds in their own houses.

And the moon shone in the window of Tonio, the Manhole Man, and crossed his face.

And the moon shone on Joe, and crossed his face.

And it shone on the Telephone Man, and the Wrecking Truck Man, and the Steam Roller Man, and the Tar Wagon Man, and the Road Boss Man.

And it shone on the Cement-mixing Man, and the Painter Man, and the Carpenter Man.

And it shone on the clouds in the dark night air.

Fix it, fix it, where are the Fix-it Men?
Sound asleep in a moonlit sleep,
Or wide awake whenever things break.
Fix it, fix it, there are the Fix-it Men.

The Lad Who Went to the North Wind

illustrated by ELIZABETH SKILTON

Once on a time there was an old widow who had one son and as she was poorly and weak, her son had to go up into the pantry to fetch meal for cooking; but when he got outside the pantry and was just going down the steps, there came the North Wind, puffing and blowing, caught up the meal, and so away with it through the air. Then the lad

A Norse folk tale by Peter Christen Askjørnsen and Jørgen Engebretsen Moe, translated by George Webbe Dasent.

went back into the pantry for more; but when he came out again on the steps, if the North Wind didn't come again and carry off the meal with a puff; and more than that, he did so the third time. At this the lad got very angry; and as he thought it hard that the North Wind should behave so, he thought he'd just look him up, and ask him to give up his meal.

So off he went, but the way was long, and he walked and walked; but at last he came to the North Wind's house.

"Good day!" said the lad. "And thank you for coming to see us yesterday."

"GOOD DAY!" answered the North Wind, for his voice was loud and gruff. "AND THANKS FOR COMING TO SEE ME. WHAT DO YOU WANT?"

"Oh!" answered the lad, "I only wished to ask you to be so good as to let me have back that meal you took

from me on the pantry steps, for we haven't much to live on; and if you're to go on snapping up the morsel we have there'll be nothing for it but to starve."

"I haven't got your meal," said the North Wind; "but if you are in such need, I'll give you a cloth which will get you everything you want, if you only say, 'Cloth, spread yourself, and serve up all kind of good dishes!'"

With this the lad was well content. But, as the way was so long he couldn't get home in one day, he turned into an inn on the way; and when they were going to sit down to supper, he laid the cloth on a table which stood in the corner and said—

"Cloth, spread yourself, and serve up all kind of good dishes."

He had scarce said so before the cloth did as it was bid; and all who stood by thought it a fine thing, but most of all the landlady. So, when all were fast asleep, at dead of night, she took the lad's cloth, and put another in its stead, just like the one he had got from the North Wind, but which couldn't so much as serve up a bit of dry bread.

So, when the lad woke, he took his cloth and went off with it, and that day he got home to his mother.

"Now," said he, "I've been to the North Wind's house, and a good fellow he is, for he gave me this cloth, and when I only say to it, 'Cloth, spread yourself, and serve up all kind of good dishes,' I get any sort of food I please."

"All very true, I daresay," said his mother; "but seeing is believing, and I shan't believe it till I see it."

So the lad made haste, drew out a table, laid the cloth

on it, and said—

"Cloth, spread yourself, and serve up all kind of good dishes."

But never a bit of dry bread did the cloth serve up.

"Well," said the lad, "there's no help for it but to go to the North Wind again"; and away he went.

So he came to where the North Wind lived late in the afternoon.

"Good evening!" said the lad.

"Good evening!" said the North Wind.

"I want my rights for that meal of ours which you took," said the lad; "for as for that cloth I got, it isn't worth a penny."

"I've got no meal," said the North Wind; "but yonder you have a ram which coins nothing but golden ducats as soon as you say to it—

"'Ram, ram! make money!'"

So the lad thought this a fine thing; but as it was too

far to get home that day, he turned in for the night to the same inn where he had slept before.

Before he called for anything, he tried the truth of what the North Wind had said to the ram, and found it all right; but when the landlord saw that, he thought it was a famous ram, and when the lad had fallen asleep, he took another which couldn't coin gold ducats, and changed the two.

Next morning off went the lad; and when he got home to his mother, he said—

"After all, the North Wind is a jolly fellow; for now he has given me a ram which can coin golden ducats if I only say, 'Ram, ram! make money!'"

"All very true, I daresay," said his mother; "but I shan't believe any such stuff until I see the ducats made."

"Ram, ram! Make money!" said the lad; but the ram made nothing.

So the lad went back again to the North Wind, and blew him up, and said the ram was worth nothing, and he must have his rights for the meal.

"Well," said the North Wind; "I've nothing else to give you but that old stick in the corner yonder; but it's a stick of that kind that if you say—

"'Stick, stick! lay on!' it lays on till you say—

"'Stick, stick! now stop!'"

So, as the way was long, the lad turned in this night, too, to the landlord; but as he could pretty well guess how things stood as to the cloth and the ram, he lay down at once on the bench and began to snore, as if he were asleep.

Now the landlord, who easily saw that the stick must

be worth something, hunted up one which was like it, and when he heard the lad snore, was going to change the two, but just as the landlord was about to take it the lad bawled out—

"Stick, stick! lay on!"

So the stick began to beat the landlord, till he jumped over chairs, and tables, and benches, and yelled and roared—

"Oh my! oh my! bid the stick be still, else it will beat me to death, and you shall have back both your cloth and your ram."

When the lad thought the landlord had got enough, he said—

"Stick, stick! now stop!"

Then he took the cloth and put it into his pocket, and went home with his stick in his hand, leading the ram by a cord round its horns; and so he got his rights for the meal he had lost.

Let's Go to Belgium

Belgium is a small, beautiful European country surrounded by the Netherlands, Germany, Luxemburg, and France. Except for the Ardennes Plateau, it is a low-lying country, crisscrossed by more than 100 waterways. One city, Bruges, has over 50 bridges that cross the canals.

Oats, rye, wheat, barley, sugar beets, vegetables, and livestock are raised on the farms. Over half of Belgium's rich soil, some of it reclaimed from the sea, is under cultivation. Farmers often have to wear wooden shoes to keep their feet dry in the marshy fields.

Belgium is also one of the most industrialized countries in the world. She has great coal resources, and important steel, chemical, textile, and diamond cutting industries. Canals and railroads make her a leader in transportation.

This nation has had a long, troubled history. At various times she was ruled by the Romans, by Spain, Austria, Germany, and France. But in 1830 the Belgians declared their independence. Their constitution, modeled in some ways after that of the United States, created a liberal and democratic constitutional monarchy.

In Belgium two different languages are spoken, Flemish in the north and French in the south. But this fact does not prevent the industrious and energetic Belgians from working together. Despite severe losses of manpower and homes and factories in World Wars I and II, these skilled people have provided a good life for themselves.

156

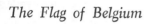

The Flag of Belgium

Medieval castle in Ghent

Canals, like this one in Bruges, are important to Belgium.

Can you find the following things on the map? **1.** Seacoast fisherman **2.** Belgian work horse **3.** Tapestry weaver **4.** Woman making lace **5.** Grapes growing in greenhouse **6.** Picturesque medieval town square **7.** 13th century church **8.** Typical outdoor market **9.** Milk cart pulled by dog **10.** King Leopold's majestic Arch of Triumph **11.** Sheep that provide fine wool

GERMANY

Luxemburg

MONTZEN

GENK

4

9

LIEGE

2

MANDERFELD

RIVER

NAMUR

E. R.

RE R.

7

DINANT

TTET

ARLON

5

FLORENVILLE

COUVIN

MEUSE

N

E

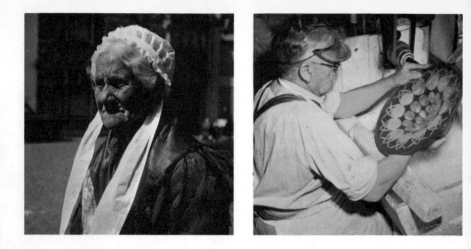

Belgium is famous throughout the world for her craftsmen and their beautiful products. *Left,* a Flemish lace maker wearing her handiwork on her head. *Right,* a glass cutter practices a traditional and painstaking Belgian art.

Almost all Belgians are devout Catholics. *Left,* in medieval costume, the Procession of the Sacred Blood. *Right,* Palace of the Cinquantenaire, Brussels. All through history Belgium has produced outstanding art and architecture.